COUNSELS BY THE WAY

COUNSELS
BY THE
WAY

BY
HENRY VAN DYKE

NEW YORK
THOMAS Y. CROWELL & CO.
PUBLISHERS

COMPOSITION AND ELECTROTYPE PLATES BY
D. B. UPDIKE, THE MERRYMOUNT PRESS, BOSTON

DEDICATED IN FRIENDSHIP
TO JOHN HUSTON FINLEY
PRESIDENT OF THE COLLEGE OF THE
CITY OF NEW YORK

PUBLISHERS' NOTE

FROM time to time the present publishers have brought out separate essays by Dr. Van Dyke, under such distinctive titles as "Ships and Havens" (1897), "The Poetry of the Psalms" (1900), and "Joy and Power" (1903). These little books, each done in special type and printed in black and red, have found many thousands of readers. But requests have been received for a single volume containing all this material, in order that it may be preserved in permanent library form, and we have therefore issued the present book. The little gift books containing single essays may still be had as formerly.

CONTENTS

3

SHIPS AND HAVENS

SHIPS AND HAVENS

I

PILGRIMS OF THE SEA

OF all the things that man has made, none is so full of interest and charm, none possesses so distinct a life and character of its own, as a ship.

"Ships are but boards," says Shylock in "The Merchant of Venice." But we feel that this is a thoroughly wooden opinion, one of those literal judgements which stick to the facts and miss the truth. Ships have something more in them than the timbers of which they are made. Human thought and human labour and human love; the designer's clever conception, the builder's patient toil, the explorer's daring venture, the merchant's costly enterprise, the sailor's loyal affection, the traveller's hopes and fears,—all the manifold sympathies of humanity,—inform the dumb pilgrims of the sea with a human quality. There is a spirit within their oaken ribs, a significance in their strange histories.

[3]

The common language in which we speak of them is an unconscious confession of this feeling. We say of a ship, "She sails well. She minds her helm quickly. The wind is against her, but she makes good headway. We wish her a prosperous voyage." We endow her with personality; and, as if to acknowledge the full measure of our interest, we express it in terms which belong to the more interesting sex.

One reason for this is undoubtedly the fact that the ship appears to us as a traveller to an unseen, and often an unknown, haven. It is the element of mystery, of adventure, of movement towards a secret goal, that fascinates our imagination, and draws our sympathy after it. When this is wanting, the ship loses something of her enchantment.

There is a little cottage where I have spent many summers on the sleepy southern shore of Long Island. From the white porch we could look out upon a shallow, land-locked bay. There we saw, on every sunny day, a score of sailboats, flickering to and fro on the bright circle of water in swal-

low-flights, with no aim but their own motion in the pleasant breeze. It was a flock
of little play-ships,—a pretty sight, but it
brought no stir to the thought, no thrill to
the emotions.

From the upper windows of the house
the outlook surpassed a long line of ragged
sand-dunes, and ranged across

> The unplumbed, salt, estranging sea.

There went the real ships, of all shapes
and sizes, of all rigs and models; the great
steamers, building an airy pillar of cloud by
day, a flashing pillar of fire by night; the
ragged coasters, with their patched and
dingy sails; the slim, swift yachts, hurry-
ing by in gala dress, as if in haste to arrive
at some distant, merry festival of Neptune's
court. Sometimes they passed in groups,
like flights of plover; sometimes in single
file, like a flock of wild swans; sometimes
separate and lonely, one appearing and van-
ishing before the next hove in sight.

When the wind was from the north they
hugged the shore. With a glass one could
see the wrinkled, weather-beaten face of the

man at the wheel, and the short pipe smoking between his lips. When the wind was southerly and strong they kept far away, creeping slowly along the rim of the horizon. On a fair breeze they dashed along, wing and wing, with easy, level motion. When the wind was contrary they came beating in and out, close-hauled, tossing and labouring over the waves. It was a vision of endless variety and delight. But behind it all, giving life and interest to the scene, was the invisible thought of the desired haven.

Whither is she travelling, that long, four-masted schooner, with all her sails set to catch the fickle northwest breeze? Is it in some languid bay of the West Indies, or in some rocky harbour of Patagonia, amid the rigours of the far southern winter, that she will cast anchor? Where is she bound, that dark little tramp-steamer, trailing voluminous black smoke behind her, and buffeting her way to the eastward in the teeth of the rising gale? Is it in some sunlit port among the bare purple hills of Spain, or in the cool shadows of some forest-clad Norwegian fiord, that she will find her moorings? Whither away, ye ships? What haven?

How often, and how exquisitely, this question of ships and havens has been expressed by the poets (in prose and verse), who translate our thoughts for us. Longfellow recalls a dream of his childhood in the seaport town of Portland:

> I remember the black wharves and the slips,
> And the sea-tides tossing free;
> And Spanish sailors with bearded lips,
> And the beauty and mystery of the ships,
> And the magic of the sea.
> And the voice of that wayward song
> Is singing and saying still:
> "A boy's will is the wind's will,
> And the thoughts of youth are long, long
> thoughts."

George William Curtis wanders down to the Battery, and meditates on "Sea from Shore:" "The sails were shaken out, and the ship began to move. It was a fair breeze perhaps, and no steamer was needed to tow her away. She receded down the bay. Friends turned back,—I could not see them,—and waved their hands, and wiped their eyes, and went home to dinner. Farther and farther from the ships at anchor, the lessening vessel became single and solitary upon the water. The sun sank in the west; but I watched her still. Every flash of her sails, as she tacked and turned, thrilled my heart. . . . I did not know the consignees nor the name of the vessel. I had shipped no adventure, nor risked any insurance, nor made any bet, but my eyes clung to her as Ariadne's to the fading sail of Theseus."

And here is a bit of Rudyard Kipling's gusty music from "The Seven Seas:"

The Liner she's a lady, an' she never looks
    nor 'eeds —
The Man-o'-War's 'er 'usband, an' 'e gives
    'er all she needs;
But, oh, the little cargo-boats, that sail the
    wet seas roun',
They're just the same as you and me, a-
    plyin' up an' down!

But it is Wordsworth, the most intimate and searching interpreter of delicate, half-formed emotions, who has given the best expression to the feeling that rises within us at sight of a journeying ship:

[8]

With ships the sea was sprinkled far and nigh
Like stars in heaven, and joyously it showed:
Some lying fast at anchor in the road,
Some veering up and down, one knew not
    why.
A goodly Vessel did I then espy
Come like a giant from a haven broad;
And lustily along the bay she strode,
Her tackling rich, and of apparel high.
This Ship was naught to me, nor I to her,
Yet I pursued her with a Lover's look;
This Ship to all the rest I did prefer:
When will she turn, and whither? She will
    brook
No tarrying: where she comes the winds
    must stir;
On went she, and due north her journey
    took.

Where lies the Land to which yon Ship
    must go?
Fresh as a lark mounting at break of day
Festively she puts forth in trim array;
Is she for tropic suns, or polar snow?
What boots the inquiry?—Neither friend
    nor foe
She cares for; let her travel where she may
She finds familiar friends, a beaten way

Ever before her, and a wind to blow.
Yet still I ask, what haven is her mark?
And, almost as it was when ships were rare
(From time to time, like Pilgrims, here and
    there
Crossing the waters), doubt, and something
    dark,
Of the old Sea some reverential fear
Is with me at thy farewell, joyous Bark!

And is not this a parable, beautiful and suggestive, of the way in which we look out, in our thoughtful moods, upon the ocean of human life, and the men and women who are voyaging upon it? In them also the deepest element of interest is that they are in motion. They are all going somewhither. They are not stationary objects in our view. They are not even, in this aspect, parts of the great tide of being in which they float. They are distinct, individual, separate. We single them out one by one. Each one is a voyager, with a port to seek, a course to run, a fortune to experience. The most interesting question that we can ask in regard to them is: Whither bound? What haven?

But this inquiry comes to us now not as an idle or a curious question. For, first of all, we feel that these men and women are not strangers to us. We know why we take a personal interest in one more than in another. We know why we "pursue them with a lover's look." It is as if the "joyous Bark" carried some one that we knew, as if we could see a familiar face above the bulwarks, and hear a well-beloved voice hailing us across the waves. And then we realize that we also are *en voyage*. We do not stand on the shore as spectators; we, too, are out on the ocean, sailing. All the "reverential fear of the old Sea," the peril, the mystery, the charm, of the voyage, come home to our own experience. The question becomes pressing, urgent, importunate, as we enter into the depth of its meaning. Surely there is nothing that we can ever ask ourselves in which we have a closer, deeper interest, or to which we need to find a clearer, truer answer, than this simple, direct question: *What is our desired haven in the venturesome voyage of life?*

II

WHITHER BOUND?

I WANT to talk with you about this question in this little book, as a writer may talk with a reader across the unknown intervals of time and space. The book that does **not** really speak to you is not worth much. And unless you really hear something, and make some kind of an answer to it, you do not truly read.

There is a disadvantage, of course, in the fact that you and I do not know each other and speak face to face. Who you are into whose hands this book has come, I cannot tell. And to you, I am nothing but a name. Where you may be while you turn these pages, I cannot guess. Perhaps you are sitting in your own quiet room after a hard day's work; perhaps you are reading aloud in some circle of friends around the open fire; perhaps you are in the quiet woods, or out in the pleasant orchard under your favourite tree; perhaps you are actually on the deck of a ship travelling across the waters. It is strange and wonderful to think of the many different places into which the words that I am now writing in this lonely, book-lined study may come, and of the many different eyes that may read them.

But wherever you are, and whoever you may be, there is one thing in which you and I are just alike at this moment, and in all the moments of our existence. We are not at rest; we are on a journey. Our life is not a mere fact; it is a movement, a tendency, a steady, ceaseless progress towards an unseen goal. We are gaining something, or losing something, every day. Even when our position and our character seem to remain precisely the same, they are changing. For the mere advance of time is a change. It is not the same thing to have a bare field in January and in July. The season makes the difference. The limitations that are childlike in the child are childish in the man.

Everything that we do is a step in one direction or another. Even the failure to do something is in itself a deed. It sets us forward or backward. The action of the negative pole of a magnetic needle is just as

[13]

real as the action of the positive pole. To decline is to accept—the other alternative.

Are you richer to-day than you were yesterday? No? Then you are a little poorer. Are you better to-day than you were yesterday? No? Then you are a little worse. Are you nearer to your port to-day than you were yesterday? Yes,—you must be a little nearer to some port or other; for since your ship was first launched upon the sea of life, you have never been still for a single moment; the sea is too deep, you could not find an anchorage if you would; there can be no pause until you come into port.

But what is it, then, the haven towards which you are making? What is the goal that you desire and hope to reach? What is the end of life towards which you are drifting or steering?

There are three ways in which we may look at this question, depending upon the point of view from which we regard human existence.

When we think of it as a work, the question is, "What do we desire to accomplish?"

When we think of it as a growth, a development, a personal unfolding, the question is, "What do we desire to become?"

When we think of it as an experience, a destiny, the question is, "What do we desire to become of us?"

Do not imagine for an instant that these questions can be really separated. They are interwoven. They cross each other from end to end of the web of life. The answer to one question determines the answer to the others. We cannot divide our work from ourselves, nor isolate our future from our qualities. A ship might as well try to sail north with her jib, and east with her foresail, and south with her mainsail, as a man to go one way in conduct, and another way in character, and another way in destiny.

What we do belongs to what we are; and what we are is what becomes of us.

And yet, as a matter of fact, there is a difference in these three standpoints from which we may look at our life; and this difference not only makes a little variation in the view that we take of our existence, but also influences unconsciously our manner

of thinking and speaking about it. Most of
the misunderstandings that arise when we
are talking about life come from a failure
to remember this. We are looking at the
same thing, but we are looking from oppo-
site corners of the room. We are discussing
the same subject, but in different dialects.

Some people—perhaps the majority—
are of a practical turn of mind. Life seems
to them principally an affair of definite
labour directed to certain positive results.
They are usually thinking about what they
are to do in the world, and what they are
to get for it. It is a question of occupation,
of accomplishment, of work and wages.

Other people—and I think almost all
serious-minded people when they are young,
and life still appears fresh and wonderful
to them—regard their existence from the
standpoint of sentiment, of feeling, of personality. They have their favourite characters in history or fiction, whom they admire
and try to imitate. They have their ideals,
which they seek and hope to realize. Some
vision of triumph over obstacles, and victory over enemies, some model of manhood

or womanhood, shines before them. By that standard they test and measure themselves. Towards that end they direct their efforts. The question of life, for them, is a question of attainment, of self-discipline, of self-development.

Other people—and I suppose we may say all people at some time or other in their experience—catch a glimpse of life in still wider and more mysterious relations. They see that it is not really, for any one of us, an independent and self-centred and self-controlled affair. They feel that its issues run out far beyond what we can see in this world. They have a deep sense of a future state of being towards which we are all inevitably moving. This movement cannot be a matter of chance. It must be under law, under responsibility, under guidance. It cannot be a matter of indifference to us. It ought to be the object of our most earnest concern, our most careful choice, our most determined endeavour. If there is a port beyond the horizon, we should know where it lies and how to win it. And so the question of life, in these profound moods which come to all of us, presents itself as a question of eternal destiny.

Now, if we are to understand each other, if we are to get a view of the subject which shall be anything like a well-rounded view, a complete view, we must look at the question from all three sides. We must ask ourselves: What is our desired haven, first, in achievement; and second, in character; and last, in destiny?

III

THE HAVEN OF WORK

SURELY we ought to know what it is that we really want to do in the world, what practical result we desire to accomplish with our lives. And this is a question which it will be very wise to ask and answer before we determine what particular means we shall use in order to perform our chosen work and to secure the desired result. A man ought to know what he proposes to make before he selects and prepares his tools. A captain should have a clear idea of what port he is to reach before he attempts to lay his course and determine his manner of sailing.

All these minor questions of ways and means must come afterwards. They cannot be settled at the outset. They depend on circumstances. They change with the seasons. There are many paths to the same end. One may be best to-day; another may be best to-morrow. The wind and the tide make a difference. One way may be best

for you, another way for me. The build of
the ship must be taken into consideration.
A flat-bottomed craft does best in the shallow water, along shore. A deep keel is for
the open sea.

But before we make up our minds how
to steer from day to day, we must know
where we are going in the long run. Then
we can shape our course to fit our purpose.
We can learn how to meet emergencies as
they arise. We can change our direction to
avoid obstacles and dangers. We can take
a roundabout way if need be. If we keep
the thought of our desired haven clearly before us, all the other points can be more
easily and wisely settled; and however de-
vious and difficult the voyage may be, it
will be a success when we get there.

I am quite sure that a great deal of the
confusion and perplexity of youth, and a
great deal of the restlessness and fickleness
which older people often criticise so severely
and so unjustly, come from the attempt to
choose an occupation in life before the
greater question of the real object of our
life-work has been fairly faced and settled.

[20]

"What are you going to do when you grow up?" This is the favourite conundrum which the kind aunts and uncles put to the boys when they come home from school; and of late they are beginning to put it to the girls also, since it has been reluctantly admitted that a girl may rightly have something to say about what she would like to do in the world. But how is it possible to make anything more than a blind guess at the answer, unless the boy or the girl has some idea of the practical end which is to be worked for. To choose a trade, a business, a profession, without knowing what kind of a result you want to get out of your labour, is to set sail in the dark. It is to have a course, but no haven; an employment, but no vocation.

There are really only four great practical ends for which men and women can work in this world,— Pleasure, Wealth, Fame, and Usefulness. We owe it to ourselves to consider them carefully, and to make up our minds which of them is to be our chief object in life.

Pleasure is one aim in life, and there are

[21]

a great many people who are following it, consciously or unconsciously, as the main end of all their efforts. Now, pleasure is a word which has a double meaning. It may mean the satisfaction of all the normal desires of our manhood in their due proportion, and in this sense it is a high and noble end. There is a pleasure in the intelligent exercise of all our faculties, in the friendship of nature, in the perception of truth, in the generosity of love, in the achievements of heroism, in the deeds of beneficence, in the triumphs of self-sacrifice. "It is not to taste sweet things," says Carlyle, "but to do true and noble things, and vindicate himself under God's Heaven as a God-made man, that the poorest son of Adam dimly longs. Show him the way of doing that, the dullest day-drudge kindles into a hero."

But pleasure as we commonly speak of it means something very different from this. It denotes the immediate gratification of our physical senses and appetites and inclinations. There is a free gift of pleasant sensation attached by the Creator to the fulfilment of our natural propensions. The taking of food, for example, not only nourishes the body, but also gratifies the palate; the quenching of thirst is agreeable to the senses as well as necessary to the maintenance of life. No sane and wholesome thinker has ventured to deny that it is lawful and wise to receive this gratuitous gift of pleasure, and rejoice in it, as it comes to us in this world wherein God has caused to grow "every tree that is pleasant to the sight and good for food." But when we make the reception of the agreeable sensation the chief end and motive of our action, when we direct our will and our effort to the attainment of this end, then we enter upon a pleasure-seeking life. We make that which should be our servant to refresh and cheer us, our master to direct and rule and drive us.

The evil nature of this transformation is suggested in the very names which we give to human conduct in which the gratification of the senses has become the controlling purpose. The man who lives for the sake of the enjoyment that he gets out of eating and drinking is a glutton or a drunkard.

[23]

The man who measures the success and happiness of his life by its physical sensations, whether they be coarse and brutal or delicate and refined, is a voluptuary.

A pleasure-seeking life, in this sense, when we think of it clearly and carefully, is one which has no real end or goal outside of itself. Its aim is unreal and transitory, a passing thrill in nerves that decay, an experience that leads nowhere, and leaves nothing behind it. Robert Burns knew the truth of what he wrote:

> But pleasures are like poppies spread,
> You seize the flower, the bloom is shed!

The man who chooses pleasure as the object of his life has no real haven, but is like a boat that beats up and down and drifts to and fro, merely to feel the motion of the waves and the impulse of the wind. When the voyage of life is done he has reached no port, he has accomplished nothing.

One of the wisest of the ancients, the Stoic philosopher Seneca, wrote a letter to his brother Gallio (the Roman governor before whom St. Paul was tried in Corinth), in which he speaks very frankly about the folly of a voluptuous life. "Those who have permitted pleasure to lead the van . . . lose virtue altogether; and yet they do not possess pleasure, but *are possessed by it*, and are either tortured by its absence, or choked by its excess, being wretched if deserted by it, and yet more wretched if overwhelmed by it; like those who are caught in the shoals of the Syrtes, and at one time are stranded on dry ground, and at another tossed on the furious billows. . . . As we hunt wild beasts with toil and peril, and even when they are caught find them an anxious possession, for they often tear their keepers to pieces, even so are great pleasures: they turn out to be great evils, and take their owners prisoner."

This is the voice of human prudence and philosophy. The voice of religion is even more clear and piercing. St. Paul says of the pleasure-seekers: "Whose end is destruction, whose god is their belly, whose glory is their shame, who mind earthly things." And in another place, lest we should forget that this is as true of women as it is

of men, he says: "She that liveth in pleasure is dead while she liveth." That saying
is profoundly true. It goes to the bottom of
the subject. A pleasure-seeking life is a living death, because its object perishes even
while it is attained, and at the end nothing
is left of it but dust and corruption.

Think of the result of existence in the
man or woman who has lived chiefly to
gratify the physical appetites; think of its
real emptiness, its real repulsiveness, when
old age comes, and the senses are dulled,
and the roses have faded, and the lamps at
the banquet are smoking and expiring, and
desire fails, and all that remains is the fierce,
insatiable, ugly craving for delights which
have fled for evermore; think of the bitter,
burning vacancy of such an end,—and you
must see that pleasure is not a good haven
to seek in the voyage of life.

But what of wealth as a desired haven?
When we attempt to consider this subject
we have especial need to follow Dr. Sam-
uel Johnson's blunt advice and "clear our
minds of cant." There is a great deal of foolish railing against wealth, which takes for

granted, now that it is an unsubstantial and illusory good, and now that it is not a good at all, but only an unmixed evil, and the root of all other evils. Many preachers and moralists talk about wealth in this way, but they do not really think about it in this way. They know better. And when young people discover and observe the curious inconsistency between the teacher's words and his thoughts, as illuminated by his conduct, they are likely to experience a sense of disappointment, and a serious revulsion from doctrine which does not seem to be sincere.

Wealth is simply the visible result of human labour, or of the utilization of natural forces and products, in such a form that it can be exchanged. A gallon of water in a mountain lake is not wealth. But the same gallon of water conveyed through an aqueduct and delivered in the heart of a great city represents a certain amount of wealth, because it has a value in relation to the wants of men. A tree growing in an inaccessible forest is not wealth. But a stick of timber which can be delivered in a place

[27]

where men are building houses is a bit of wealth.

Now, the symbol and measure of wealth is money. It is the common standard by which the value of different commodities is estimated, and the means by which they are exchanged. It is not a dream nor a delusion. It is something real and solid. It is deserving of our respect under certain conditions and within certain limitations. The man who professes an absolute contempt for money is either a little of a fool or a good deal of a fraud. It represents a product of labour and a form of power. It is worth working for. When a man has won it, there it is—a fact and a force. He can handle it, use it, dispose of it, as he chooses.

But stop a moment; let us think! Is that altogether true? It is partly true, no doubt; for every particle of wealth, or of its symbol, money, is an actual possession of which its owner can dispose. But it is not the whole truth; for the fact is that he *must* dispose of it, because that is the only way in which it becomes available as wealth. A piece of money in an old stocking is no more than

a leaf upon a tree. It is only when the coin
is taken out and used that it becomes of
value. And the nature of the value depends
upon the quality of the use.

Moreover, it is not true that a man can
dispose of his money *as he chooses*. The purposes for which it can be used are strictly
bounded. There are many things that he
cannot buy with it; for example, health, long
life, wisdom, a cheerful spirit, a clear conscience, peace of mind, a contented heart.

You never see the stock called Happiness quoted on the exchange. How high
would it range, think you,—a hundred
shares of Happiness Preferred, guaranteed
seven per cent, seller thirty?

And there are some things that a man
cannot do with his wealth. For instance, he
cannot carry it with him when he dies. No
system of transfer has been established between the two worlds; and a large balance
here does not mean a balance on the other
side of the grave. The property of Dives
did not fall in value when he died, and yet
he became a pauper in the twinkling of an
eye.

[29]

There is no question but that those who live to win wealth in this world have a more real and substantial end in view than the mere pleasure-seekers. But the thing that we ought to understand and remember is precisely what that end is. It is the acquisition in our hands of a certain thing whose possession is very brief, and whose value depends entirely upon the use to which it is put. Now, if we make the mere gaining of that thing the desired haven of our life, we certainly spend our strength for naught, and our labour for that which satisfieth not. We narrow and contract our whole existence. We degrade it by making it terminate upon something which is only a sign, a symbol, behind which we see no worthy and enduring reality. It is for this reason that the "blind vice" of avarice, as Juvenal calls it, has been particularly despised by the wise of all lands and ages. There is no other fault that so quickly makes the heart small and hard.

They soon grow old who grope for gold
In marts where all is bought and sold;
Who live for self, and on some shelf

In darkened vaults hoard up their pelf;
Cankered and crusted o'er with mould,
For them their youth itself is old.

Nor is there any other service that appears
more unprofitable and ridiculous in the end,
when the reward for which the money-maker
has given his life is stripped away from him
with a single touch, and he is left with his
trouble for his pains.

If thou art rich, thou'rt poor;
For like an ass whose back with ingots bows,
Thou bear'st thy heavy burden but a journey,
And death unloads thee.

But perhaps you imagine that no one is in
danger of making that mistake, no one is
so foolish as to seek wealth merely for its
own sake. Do you think so? Then, what
shall we say of that large class of men, so
prominent and so influential in modern society, whose energies are desperately consecrated to the winning of great fortunes?

So far as their life speaks for them, they
have no real ambition beyond that. They
are not the leaders in noble causes, the sus-
tainers of beneficent enterprises. They have

no refined and elevated tastes to gratify. They are not the promoters of art or science, the adorners of their city with splendid buildings, the supporters of humane and beautiful charities. They have no large plans, no high and generous purposes. They have no public spirit, only an intense private greed. All that we can say of them is that they are rich, and that they evidently want to be richer.

They sit like gigantic fowls brooding upon nests of golden eggs, which never hatch. Their one desire is not to bring anything out of the eggs, but to get more eggs into their nest. It is a form of lunacy,—auromania.

But let us not suppose that these notorious examples are the only ones who are touched with this insanity. It is just the same in the man who is embittered by failure, as in the man who is elated by success; just the same in those who make it the chief end of life to raise their hundreds of dollars to thousands, as in those who express their ambition in terms of seven figures. Covetousness is idolatry of wealth. It may be paid to a little idol as well as to a big

[32]

one. Avarice may be married to Poverty, and then its offspring is named Envy; or it may be married to Riches, and then its children are called Purse-pride and Meanness. Some people sell their lives for heaps of treasure, and some for a scant thirty pieces of silver, and some for nothing better than a promissory note of fortune, without endorsement.

There are multitudes of people in the world to-day who are steering and sailing for Ophir, simply because it is the land of gold. What will they do if they reach their desired haven? They do not know. They do not even ask the question. They will be rich. They will sit down on their gold.

Let us look our desires squarely in the face! To win riches, to have a certain balance in the bank and a certain rating on the exchange, is a real object, a definite object; but it is a frightfully small object for the devotion of a human life, and a bitterly disappointing reward for the loss of an immortal soul. If wealth is our desired haven, we may be sure that it will not satisfy us when we reach it.

Well, then, what shall we say of fame as

the chief end of life? Here, again, we must be careful to discriminate between the thing itself and other things which are often confused with it. Fame is simply what our fellow-men think and say of us. It may be world-wide; it may only reach to a single country or city; it may be confined to a narrow circle of society. Translated in one way, fame is glory; translated in another way, it is merely notoriety. It is a thing which exists, of course; for the thoughts of other people about us are just as actual as our thoughts about ourselves, or as the character and conduct with which those thoughts are concerned. But the three things do not always correspond.

You remember what Dr. Oliver Wendell Holmes says, in "The Autocrat of the Breakfast-Table," about the three Johns:

1. The real John; known only to his Maker.

2. John's ideal John; never the real one, and often very unlike him.

3. Thomas's ideal John; never the real John, nor John's John, but often very unlike either.

[34]

Now, the particular object of the life that makes fame its goal is this last John. Its success consists in the report of other people's thoughts and remarks about us. Bare, naked fame, however great it may be, can never bring us anything more than an instantaneous photograph of the way we look to other men.

Consider what it is worth. It may be good or bad, flattering or painfully truthful. People are celebrated sometimes for their vices, sometimes for their follies. Anything out of the ordinary line will attract notice. Notoriety may be purchased by a colossal extravagance or a monumental absurdity. A person has been made notorious simply by showing himself "more kinds of a fool" than any one else in the community.

Many men would be famous for their vanity alone, if it were not so common that it no longer serves as a mark of distinction. We often fancy that we are occupying a large place in the attention of the world, when really we do not even fill a pin-hole.

To be governed in our course of life by a timorous consideration of what the world will think of us is to be even lighter and more fickle than a weathercock. It is to be blown about by winds so small and slight that they could not even lift a straw outside of our own versatile imagination. For what is "the world," for whose admiration, or envy, or mere notice, we are willing to give so much? "Mount up," says a wise man, "in a monomania of vanity, the number of those who bestow some passing thought upon you, as high as you dare; and what is this 'world' but a very few miserable items of human existence, which, when they disappear, none will miss, any more than they will miss thyself?"

There is one point in which fame differs very essentially from wealth and pleasure. If it comes to us without being well earned it cannot possibly be enjoyed. A pleasure may arrive by chance, and still it will be pleasant. A sum of money may be won by a gambler, and still it is real money; he can spend it as he pleases. But fame without a corresponding merit is simply an unmitigated burden. I cannot imagine a more miserable position than that of the poor scrib-

bler who allowed his acquaintances to con-
gratulate him as the writer of George Eliot's
early stories. To have the name of great
wisdom, and at the same time to be a very
foolish person, is to walk through the world
in a suit of armour so much too big and
too heavy for you that it makes every step
a painful effort. To have a fine reputation
and a mean character is to live a lie and die
a sham. And this is the danger to which
every one who seeks directly and primarily
for fame is exposed.

One thing is certain in regard to fame:
for most of us it will be very brief in itself;
for all of us it will be transient in our enjoyment of it.

When death has dropped the curtain we
shall hear no more applause. And though
we fondly dream that it will continue after
we have left the stage, we do not realize how
quickly it will die away in silence, while the
audience turns to look at the new actor and
the next scene. Our position in society will
be filled as soon as it is vacated, and our
name remembered only for a moment,—except, please God, by a few who have learned

to love us, not because of fame, but because we have helped them and done them some good.

This thought brings us, you see, within clear sight of the fourth practical aim in life, —the one end that is really worth working for,—usefulness. To desire and strive to be of some service to the world, to aim at doing something which shall really increase the happiness and welfare and virtue of mankind—this is a choice which is possible for all of us; and surely it is a good haven to sail for.

The more we think of it, the more attractive and desirable it becomes. To do some work that is needed, and to do it thoroughly well; to make our toil count for something in adding to the sum total of what is actually profitable for humanity; to make two blades of grass grow where one grew before, or, better still, to make one wholesome idea take root in a mind that was bare and fallow; to make our example count for something on the side of honesty, and cheerfulness, and courage, and good faith, and love—this is an aim for life which is very wide, as wide as the world, and yet very definite, as clear as light. It is not in the least vague. It is only free; it has the power to embody itself in a thousand forms without changing its character. Those who seek it know what it means, however it may be expressed. It is real and genuine and satisfying. There is nothing beyond it, because there can be no higher practical result of effort. It is the translation, through many languages, of the true, divine purpose of all the work and labour that is done beneath the sun, into one final, universal word. It is the active consciousness of personal harmony with the will of God who worketh hitherto.

To have this for the chief aim in life ennobles and dignifies all that it touches. Wealth that comes as the reward of usefulness can be accepted with honour; and, consecrated to further usefulness, it becomes royal. Fame that comes from noble service, the gratitude of men, be they few or many, to one who has done them good, is true glory; and the influence that it brings is as near to godlike power as anything that man can attain. But whether these temporal rewards are bestowed upon us or not, the real desire of the soul is satisfied just in being useful. The pleasantest word that a man can hear at the close of the day, whispered in secret to his soul, is, "Well done, good and faithful servant!"

Christ tells us this: "He that loseth his life shall find it." "Whosoever will be great among you, let him be your minister; and whosoever will be chief among you, let him be your servant."

Life is divine when duty is a joy.

Do we accept these sailing orders? Is it really the desired haven of all our activity to do some good in the world; to carry our share of the great world's burden which must be borne, to bring our lading of treasure, be it small or great, safely into the port of usefulness? I wonder how many of us have faced the question and settled it. It goes very deep.

IV

THE HAVEN OF CHARACTER

BUT deeper still the question goes when we look at it in another light. Our life is made up, not of actions alone, but of thoughts and feelings and habitual affections. These taken all together constitute what we call our present character. In their tendencies and impulses and dominant desires they constitute our future character, towards which we are moving as a ship to her haven.

What is it, then, for you and me, this intimate ideal, this distant self, this hidden form of personality which is our goal?

I am sure that we do not often enough put the problem clearly before us in this shape. We all dream of the future, especially when we are young.

A boy's will is the wind's will,
And the thoughts of youth are long, long
thoughts.

But our dreams are too much like the modern stage, full of elaborate scenery and machinery, crowded with startling effects and brilliant costumes and magical transformations, but strangely vacant of all real character.

The stuff of which our day-dreams are made is for the most part of very cheap material. We seldom weave into them the threads of our inmost spiritual life. We build castles in Spain, and forecast adventures in Bohemia. But the castle is without a real master. The hero of the adventure is vague and misty. We do not clearly recognize his face, or know what is in his heart.

We picture ourselves as living here or there; we imagine ourselves as members of a certain circle of society, taking our places among the rich, the powerful, the "smart set." We fancy ourselves going through the various experiences of life, a fortunate marriage, a successful business career, a literary triumph, a political victory. Or perhaps, if our imagination is of a more sombre type, we foreshadow ourselves in circumstances of defeat and disappointment and adversity. But in all these reveries we do

[42]

not really think deeply of our Selves. We do not stay to ask what manner of men and women we shall be, when we are living here or there, or doing thus or so.

Yet it is an important question,—very much more important, in fact, than the thousand and one trifling interrogatories about the future with which we amuse our idle hours.

And the strange thing is that, though our ideal of future character is so often hidden from us, overlooked, forgotten, it is always there, and always potently, though unconsciously, shaping our course in life. "Every one," says Cervantes, "is the son of his own works." But his works do not come out of the air, by chance. They are wrought out in a secret, instinctive harmony with a conception of character which we inwardly acknowledge as possible and likely for us.

When we choose between two lines of conduct, between a mean action and a noble one, we choose also between two persons, both bearing our name, the one representing what is best in us, the other embody-

[43]

ing what is worst. When we vacillate and alternate between them, we veer, as the man in Robert Louis Stevenson's story veered, between Dr. Jekyll and Mr. Hyde.

We say that we "make up our minds" to do a certain thing or not to do it, to resist a certain temptation or to yield to it. It is true. We "make up our minds" in a deeper sense than we remember. In every case the ultimate decision is between two future selves, one with whom the virtue is harmonious, another with whom the vice is consistent. To one of these two figures, dimly concealed behind the action, we move forward. What we forget is that, when the forward step is taken, the shadow will be *myself*. Character is eternal destiny.

There is a profound remark in George Eliot's "Middlemarch" which throws light far down into the abyss of many a lost life. "We are on a perilous margin when we begin to look passively at our future selves, and see our own figures led with dull consent into insipid misdoing and shabby achievement." But there is a brighter side to this same truth of life philosophy. We are on a path which leads upward, by sure and steady steps, when we begin to look at our future selves with eyes of noble hope and clear purpose, and see our figures climbing, with patient, dauntless effort, towards the heights of true manhood and womanhood. Visions like these are Joseph's dreams. They are stars for guidance. They are sheaves of promise. The very memory of them, if we cherish it, is a power of pure restraint and generous inspiration.

Oh, for a new generation of day-dreamers, young men and maidens who shall behold visions, idealists who shall see themselves as the heroes of coming conflicts, the heroines of yet unwritten epics of triumphant compassion and stainless love. From their hearts shall spring the renaissance of faith and hope. The ancient charm of true romance shall flow forth again to glorify the world in the brightness of their ardent eyes, —

> The light that never was on land or sea,
> The consecration and the poet's dream.

As they go out from the fair gardens of

a visionary youth into the wide, confused, turbulent field of life, they will bring with them the marching music of a high resolve. They will strive to fulfil the fine prophecy of their own best desires. They will not ask whether life is worth living,—they will make it so. They will transform the sordid "struggle for existence" into a glorious effort to become that which they have admired and loved.

But such a new generation is possible only through the regenerating power of the truth that "a man's life consisteth not in the abundance of the things that he possesseth." We must learn to recognize the real realities, and to hold them far above the perishing trappings of existence which men call real.

The glory of our life below
Comes not from what we do or what we know,
But dwells for evermore in what we are.

"He only is advancing in life," says John Ruskin, "whose heart is getting softer, whose blood warmer, whose brain quicker, whose spirit is entering into Living peace. And the men who have this life in them are the true lords or kings of the earth—they, and they only."

Now I think you can see what is meant by this question of the desired haven in character. What manner of men and women do we truly hope and wish to become?

The number of ideals seems infinite. But, after all, there are only two great types. St. Paul calls them "the carnal" and "the spiritual;" and I know of no better names.

The carnal type of character, weak or strong, clever or stupid, is always self-ruled, governed by its own appetites and passions, seeking its own ends, and, even when conformed to some outward law or code of honour, obedient only because it finds its own advantage or comfort therein. There is many a man who stands upright only because the pressure of the crowd makes it inconvenient for him to stoop. "The churl in spirit" may speak fair words because of those who hear; but in his heart he says the thing that pleases him, which is vile.

The spiritual type of character is divinely ruled, submissive to a higher law, doing another will than its own, seeking the ends of

virtue and holiness and unselfish love. It
may have many inward struggles, many de-
feats, many bitter renunciations and regrets.
It may appear far less peaceful, orderly,
self-satisfied, than some of those who are
secretly following the other ideal. Many a
saint in the making seems to be marred by
faults and conflicts from which the smug,
careful, reputable sensualist is exempt. The
difference between the two is not one of position. It is one of direction. The one, however high he stands, is moving down. The
other, however low he starts, is moving up.

We all know who it is that stands at the
very summit of the spiritual pathway,—
Jesus Christ, the Son of God, who became
a perfect man, leaving us an example that
we should follow in his steps. We know,
too, the steps in which he trod,—obedience, devotion, purity, truthfulness, kindness, resistance of temptation, self-sacrifice.
And we know the result of following him,
until we come, in the unity of the faith and
of the knowledge of the Son of God, unto a
perfect manhood, unto the measure of the
stature of the fulness of Christ.

[48]

Which type of character do we honestly desire and expect to reach? Let us not indulge in any delusions about it. Just as surely as our faces are hardening into a certain expression, ugly or pleasant, and our bodies are moving towards a certain condition of health, sound or diseased, so surely are our souls moving towards a certain type of character. Along which line are we looking and steering?—along the line that leads to an older, grayer, stiffer likeness of our present selves, with all our selfishness and pride and impurity and inconsistency and discontent confirmed and hardened; or the line that ends in likeness to Christ?

Surely we are voyaging blindly unless we know what haven of character our souls are seeking. Surely we are making a mad and base and fatal choice, unless we direct our course to the highest and the noblest goal. To know Christ is life eternal. To become like Christ is success everlasting.

V

THE LAST PORT

THERE is still one more way of putting this question about our desired haven,—a way perhaps more common than the others, and therefore probably more natural, though I cannot believe that it is more important. It is, in fact, simply a carrying on of the first two questions beyond the horizon of mortal sight, a prolongation of the voyage of life upon the ocean of eternity.

Almost all of us have an expectation, however dim and misty, of an existence of some kind after we have crossed the bar of death. Even those who do not believe that this existence will be conscious, those who suppose that death ends all, so far as our thought and feeling are concerned, and that the soul goes out when the heart stops,— even the doubters of immortality foresee a certain kind of a haven for their lives in the deep, dreamless, endless sleep of oblivion. There is no one now living who does not owe a clear and definite answer to the question: Where do you wish and expect to go when you die?

Now, I am quite sure that we have no right to try to separate this question of our haven after death from the questions in regard to our present aspirations and efforts in conduct and character. For every one who considers it soberly must see that our future destiny cannot possibly be anything else than the reward and consequence of our present life. Whether it be a state of spiritual blessedness, or an experience of spiritual woe, or simply a blank extinction, it will come as the result of the deeds done in the body. It will be the fitting and inevitable arrival at a goal towards which we have been moving in all our actions, and for which we have been preparing ourselves by all the secret affections and hopes and beliefs which we are daily working into our characters.

But there is a reason, after all, and a very profound reason, why we should sometimes put this question of our desired haven after death in a distinct form, and why we should

[51]

try to give a true and honest answer to it, with an outlook that goes beyond the grave.

It is because the answer will certainly determine our conduct now, and there is every reason to believe that it will affect the result hereafter.

Men say that the future life is only a possibility, or at best a probability, and that it is foolish to waste our present existence in the consideration of problems to which the only answer must be a "perhaps," or "I hope so," or "I believe so." But is it not one of the very conditions of our advance, even in this world, that we should be forever going forward along lines which lie altogether in the region of the probable, and for which we have no better security than our own expectation and wish that they shall lead us to the truth, anticipated, but as yet unproved and really unknown?

"So far as man stands for anything," writes Professor William James, the psychologist, in his latest book, "The Will to Believe," "and is productive or originative at all, his entire vital function may be said to have to deal with *maybes*. Not a victory is gained, not a deed of faithfulness or courage is done, except upon a maybe; not a service, not a sally of generosity, not a scientific exploration or experiment or text-book, that may not be a mistake. It is only by risking our persons from one hour to another that we live at all. And often enough our faith beforehand in an uncertified result *is the only thing that makes the result come true.*"

Surely this is certain enough in regard to the difference between this present life as a dull and dismal struggle for the meat and drink that are necessary for an animal existence, and as a noble and beautiful conflict for moral and spiritual ends. *It is the faith that makes the result come true.* As a man thinketh in his heart, so is he, and so is his world. For those whose thoughts are earthly and sensual, this is a beast's world. For those whose thoughts are high and noble and heroic, it is a hero's world. The strength of wishes transforms the very stuff of our existence, and moulds it to the form of our heart's inmost desire and hope.

Why should it not be true in the world to come? Why should not the eternal result, as well as the present course, of our voyaging depend upon our own choice of a haven beyond the grave? Christ says that it does. "Seek ye first the kingdom of God." "Lay not up for yourselves treasures upon earth, but lay up for yourselves treasures in heaven."

If the immortal life is a reality, is it not reasonable to think that the first condition of our attaining it is that we should personally wish for it, and strive to enter into it? And must not our neglect or refusal to do this be the one thing that will inevitably shut us out from it, and make our eternity an outer darkness?

Mark you, I do not say that it is reasonable to suppose that we must be absolutely certain of the reality of heaven in order to arrive thither.

We may have many doubts and misgivings. But deep down in our hearts there must be the wish to prove the truth of this great hope of an endless life with God, and the definite resolve to make this happy haven the end of all our voyaging.

This is what the apostle means by "the

[54]

power of an endless life." The passion of immortality is the thing that immortalizes our being. To be in love with heaven is the surest way to be fitted for it. Desire is the magnetic force of character. Character is the compass of life. "He that hath this hope in him purifieth himself."

Let me, then, put this question to you very simply and earnestly and personally.

What is your desired haven beyond the grave? It is for you to choose. There are no secret books of fate in which your course is traced, and your destiny irrevocably appointed. There is only the Lamb's book of life, in which new names are being written every day, as new hearts turn from darkness to light, and from the kingdom of Satan to the kingdom of God. No ship that sails the sea is as free to make for her port as you are to seek the haven that your inmost soul desires. And if your choice is right, and if your desire is real, so that you will steer and strive with God's help to reach the goal, you shall never be wrecked or lost.

For of every soul that seeks to arrive at usefulness, which is the service of Christ, and at holiness, which is the likeness of Christ, and at heaven, which is the eternal presence of Christ, it is written: *So he bringeth them unto their desired haven.*

Like unto ships far off at sea,
Outward or homeward bound, are we.
Before, behind, and all around,
Floats and swings the horizon's bound,
Seems at its distant rim to rise
And climb the crystal wall of the skies,
And then again to turn and sink
As if we could slide from its outer brink.
Ah! it is not the sea,
It is not the sea that sinks and shelves,
But ourselves
That rock and rise
With endless and uneasy motion,
Now touching the very skies,
Now sinking into the depths of ocean.
Ah! if our souls but poise and swing
Like the compass in its brazen ring,
Ever level and ever true
To the toil and the task we have to do,
We shall sail securely, and safely reach
The Fortunate Isles, on whose shining beach
The sights we see, and the sounds we hear,
Will be those of joy and not of fear.*

* Longfellow.

THE POETRY OF THE PSALMS

THE POETRY OF THE PSALMS

THIS little book is intended as a brief and simple introduction to the study of the Psalms, in English, as poetry.

There are three ways in which we may study the Bible: as a revelation, as a document, and as literature.

We may study it as the divinely inspired and perfect rule of faith and conduct. This is the point of view from which it appears most precious. For this is what we need most of all: the word of God to teach us what to believe and how to live.

We may study it as a collection of historical books, written under certain conditions, and reflecting, in their contents and in their language, the circumstances in which they were produced. This is the aspect in which criticism regards the Bible; and its intellectual interest, as well as its religious value, is greatly enhanced by a clear vision of the truth about it from this point of view.

We may study it also as literature. We may see in it a noble and impassioned interpretation of nature and life, uttered in language of beauty and sublimity, touched with the vivid colours of human personality, and embodied in forms of enduring literary art.

None of these three ways of studying the Bible is hostile to the others. On the contrary, they are helpful to one another, because each of them gives us knowledge of a real factor in the marvellous influence of the Bible in the world.

The true lover of the Bible has an interest in all the elements of its life as an immortal book. He wishes to discern, and rightly to appreciate, the method of its history, the spirit of its philosophy, the significance of its fiction, the power of its eloquence, and the charm of its poetry. He wishes this all the more because he finds in it something which is not in any other book: a vision of God, a hope for man, and an inspiration to righteousness which are evidently divine. As the worshipper in the Temple would observe the art and structure of the carven beams of cedar and the lily-work on the tops of the pillars the more

[60]

attentively because they beautified the house of his God, so the man who has a religious faith in the Bible will study more eagerly and carefully the literary forms of the book in which the Holy Spirit speaks forever.

We shall do wisely to consider and appreciate the poetical element in the Psalms. The comfort, help, and guidance that they bring to our spiritual life will not be diminished, but increased, by a perception of their exquisite form and finish. If a king sent a golden cup full of cheering cordial to a weary man, he might well admire the twofold bounty of the royal gift. The beauty of the vessel would make the draught more grateful and refreshing. And if the cup were inexhaustible, if it filled itself anew as often as it touched the lips, then the very shape and adornment of it would become significant and precious. It would be an inestimable possession, a singing goblet, a treasure of life.

John Milton, whose faith in religion was as exalted as his mastery of the art of poetry was perfect, has expressed in a single sentence the spirit in which I would approach the poetic study of the Book of Psalms: "Not in their divine arguments alone, but in the very critical art of composition, the Psalms may be easily made to appear over all kinds of lyric poetry incomparable."

I

LET us remember at the outset that a considerable part of the value of the Psalms as poetry will lie beyond the reach of this essay. We cannot precisely measure it, nor give it a full appreciation, simply because we shall be dealing with the Psalms only as we have them in our English Bible. This is a real drawback; and it will be well to state clearly the two things that we lose in reading the Psalms in this way.

First, we lose the beauty and the charm of verse. This is a serious loss. Poetry and verse are not the same thing, but they are so intimately related that it is difficult to divide them. Indeed, according to certain definitions of poetry, it would seem almost impossible.

Suppose, for example, that we accept this definition: "Poetry is that variety of the Literature of Emotion which is written in metrical form." * How, then, can we have poetry when the form is not metrical?

* *Principles of Literary Criticism.* C. T. Winchester. Page 232.

Yet who will deny that the Psalms as we have them in the English Bible are really and truly poetry?

The only way out of this difficulty that I can see is to distinguish between verse as the formal element and rhythmical emotion as the essential element in poetry. In the original production of a poem, it seems to me, it is just to say that the embodiment in metrical language is a law of art which must be observed. But in the translation of a poem (which is a kind of reflection of it in a mirror) the verse may be lost without altogether losing the poem.

Take an illustration from another art. A statue has the symmetry of solid form. You can look at it from all sides, and from every side you can see the balance and rhythm of the parts. In a photograph this solidity of form disappears. You see only a flat surface. But you still recognize it as the reflection of a statue.

The Psalms were undoubtedly written, in the original Hebrew, according to a system of versification, and perhaps to some extent with forms of rhyme.

[64]

The older scholars, like Lowth and Herder, held that such a system existed, but could not be recovered. Later scholars, like Ewald, evolved a system of their own. Modern scholarship, represented by such authors as Professors Cheyne and Briggs, is reconstructing and explaining more accurately the Hebrew versification. But, for the present at least, the only thing that is clear is that this system must remain obscure to us. It cannot be reproduced in English. The metrical versions of the Psalms are the least satisfactory. The poet Cowley said of them, "They are so far from doing justice to David that methinks they revile him worse than Shimei." * We must learn to appreciate the poetry of the Psalms without the aid of those symmetries of form and sound in which they first appeared. This is a serious loss. Poetry without verse is still poetry, but it is like a bride without a bridal garment.

The second thing that we lose in reading the Psalms in English is something even

* *The Works of Mr. Abraham Cowley.* 3 vols. London, 1710. Preface to Pindarique Odes. Volume i. page 184.

more important. It is the heavy tax on the wealth of its meaning, which all poetry must pay when it is imported from one country to another, through the medium of translation.

The most subtle charm of poetry is its suggestiveness; and much of this comes from the magical power which words acquire over memory and imagination, from their associations. This intimate and personal charm must be left behind when a poem passes from one language to another. The accompaniment, the harmony of things remembered and beloved, which the very words of the song once awakened, is silent now. Nothing remains but the naked melody of thought. If this is pure and strong, it will gather new associations; as, indeed, the Psalms have already done in English, so that their familiar expressions have become charged with musical potency. And yet I suppose such phrases as "a tree planted by the streams of water," "a fruitful vine in the innermost parts of the house," "the mountains round about Jerusalem," can never bring to us the full sense of beauty, the enlargement of heart, that they gave to the ancient Hebrews.

∴

But, in spite of this double loss, in the passage from verse to prose and from Hebrew to English, the poetry of the Psalms is so real and vital and imperishable that every reader feels its beauty and power.

It retains one valuable element of poetic form. This is that balancing of the parts of a sentence, one against another, to which Bishop Lowth first gave the familiar name of "parallelism." * The effect of this simple artifice, learned from Nature herself, is singularly pleasant and powerful. It is the rise and fall of the fountain, the ebb and flow of the tide, the tone and overtone of the chiming bell. The twofold utterance seems to bear the thought onward like the wings of a bird. A German writer compares it very exquisitely to "the heaving and sinking of the troubled heart."

It is this "parallelism" which gives such a familiar charm to the language of the

* Lowth. *De Sacra Poesi Hebraeorum Praelectiones.* Oxon., 1753.

Psalms. Unconsciously, and without recognizing the nature of the attraction, we grow used to the double cadence, the sound and the echo, and learn to look for its recurrence with delight.

> O come let us sing unto the Lord;
> Let us make a joyful noise to the rock of our
> salvation,
> Let us come before his presence with thanks-
> giving;
> And make a joyful noise unto him with psalms.

If we should want a plain English name for this method of composition we might call it *thought-rhyme*. It is easy to find varied illustrations of its beauty and of its power to emphasize large and simple ideas.

Take for instance that very perfect psalm with which the book begins—a poem so complete, so compact, so delicately wrought that it seems like a sonnet. The subject is *The Two Paths*.

The first part describes the way of the good man. It has three divisions.

The first verse gives a description of his conduct by negatives—telling us what he does not do. There is a triple thought-rhyme here.

> Blessed is the man that walketh not in the
>   counsel of the ungodly,
> Nor standeth in the way of sinners,
> Nor sitteth in the seat of the scornful.

The second verse describes his character positively, with a double thought-rhyme.

> But his delight is in the law of Jehovah;
> And in his law doth he meditate day and night.

The third verse tells us the result of this character and conduct, in a fourfold thought-rhyme.

> He shall be like a tree planted by the rivers of
>   water:
> That bringeth forth his fruit in his season:
> His leaf also shall not wither:
> And whatsoever he doeth shall prosper.

The second part of the psalm describes the way of the evil man. In the fourth verse there is a double thought-rhyme.

> The ungodly are not so:
> But are like the chaff which the wind driveth
>   away.

In the fifth verse the consequences of this worthless, fruitless, unrooted life are shown, again with a double cadence of thought, the first referring to the judgement of God, the second to the judgement of men.

> Therefore the ungodly shall not stand in the judgment:
> Nor sinners in the congregation of the righteous.

The third part of the psalm is a terse, powerful couplet, giving the reason for the different ending of the two paths.

> For Jehovah knoweth the way of the righteous:
> But the way of the ungodly shall perish.

The thought-rhyme here is one of contrast.

A poem of very different character from this brief, serious, impersonal sonnet is found in the Forty-sixth Psalm, which might be called a national anthem. Here again the poem is divided into three parts.

The first part (verses first to third) expresses a sense of joyful confidence in the Eternal, amid the tempests and confusions of earth. The thought-rhymes are in couplets; and the second phrase, in each case, emphasizes and enlarges the idea of the first phrase.

> God is our refuge and strength:
> A very present help in trouble.

The second part (verses fourth to seventh) describes the peace and security of the city of God, surrounded by furious enemies, but rejoicing in the Eternal Presence. The parallel phrases here follow the same rule as in the first part. The concluding phrase is the stronger, the more emphatic. The seventh verse gives the refrain or chorus of the anthem.

> The Lord of hosts is with us:
> The God of Jacob is our refuge.

The last part (verses eighth to tenth) describes in a very vivid and concrete way the deliverance of the people that have trusted in the Eternal. It begins with a couplet, like those which have gone before. Then follow two stanzas of triple thought-rhymes, in which the thought is stated and intensified with each repetition.

[71]

He maketh wars to cease unto the end of the
earth:
He breaketh the bow, and cutteth the spear in
sunder:
He burneth the chariot in the fire.

Be still, and know that I am God:
I will be exalted among the heathen:
I will be exalted in the earth.

The anthem ends with a repetition of the
chorus.

. .

A careful study of the Psalms, even in
English, will enable the thoughtful reader
to derive new pleasure from them, by tra-
cing the many modes and manners in which
this poetic form of thought-rhyme is used
to bind the composition together, and to
give balance and harmony to the poem.

. .

Another element of poetic form can be
discerned in the Psalms, not directly, in the
English version, but by its effects. I mean
the curious artifice of alphabetic arrange-
ment. It was a favourite practice among He-

[72]

brew poets to begin their verses with the successive letters of the alphabet, or sometimes to vary the device by making every verse in a strophe begin with one letter, and every verse in the next strophe with the following letter, and so on to the end. The Twenty-fifth and the Thirty-seventh Psalms were written by the first of these rules; the One Hundred and Nineteenth Psalm follows the second plan.

Of course the alphabetic artifice disappears entirely in the English translation. But its effects remain. The Psalms written in this manner usually have but a single theme, which is repeated over and over again, in different words and with new illustrations. They are kaleidoscopic. The material does not change, but it is turned this way and that way, and shows itself in new shapes and arrangements. These alphabetic psalms are characterized by poverty of action and richness of expression.

II

MILTON has already reminded us
that the Psalms belong to the second
of the three orders into which the Greeks,
with clear discernment, divided all poetry:
the epic, the lyric, and the dramatic. The
Psalms are rightly called lyrics because they
are chiefly concerned with the immediate
and imaginative expression of real feeling.
It is the personal and emotional note that
predominates. They are inward, confes-
sional, intense; outpourings of the quick-
ened spirit; self-revelations of the heart. It
is for this reason that we should never separate them in our thought from the actual
human life out of which they sprang. We
must feel the warm pulse of humanity in
them in order to comprehend their meaning and eternal worth. So far as we can con-
nect them with the actual experience of men,
this will help us to appreciate their reality
and power. The effort to do this will make
plain to us some other things which it is
important to remember.

[74]

We shall see at once that the book does not come from a single writer, but from many authors and ages. It represents the heart of man in communion with God through a thousand years of history, from Moses to Nehemiah, perhaps even to the time of the Maccabaean revival. It is, therefore, something very much larger and better than an individual book.

It is the golden treasury of lyrics gathered from the life of the Hebrew people. And this gives to it a singular and precious quality of brotherhood. The fault, or at least the danger, of modern lyrical poetry is that it is too solitary and separate in its tone. It tends towards exclusiveness, over-refinement, morbid sentiment. Many Christian hymns suffer from this defect. But the Psalms breathe a spirit of human fellowship even when they are most intensely personal. The poet rejoices or mourns in solitude, it may be, but not alone. He is one of the people. He is conscious always of the ties that bind him to his brother men. Compare the intense selfishness of the modern hymn:

[75]

> I can but perish if I go;
> I am resolved to try;
> For if I stay away, I know
> I shall forever die,

with the generous penitence of the Fifty-first Psalm:

> Then will I teach transgressors thy way;
> And sinners shall be converted unto thee.

It is important to observe that there are several different kinds of lyrics among the Psalms. Some of them are simple and natural outpourings of a single feeling, like *A Shepherd's Song about His Shepherd*, in the incomparable Twenty-third Psalm.

This little poem is a perfect melody. It would be impossible to express a pure, unmixed emotion—the feeling of joy in the Divine Goodness — more simply, more sweetly, with a more penetrating lyrical charm. The "valley of the death-shade," the "enemies" in whose presence the table is spread, are but dimly suggested in the background. The atmosphere of the psalm is clear and bright. The singing shepherd walks in light. The whole world is the

[76]

House of the Lord, and life is altogether gladness.

How different is the tone, the quality, of the One Hundred and Nineteenth Psalm! This is not a melody, but a harmony; not a song, but an ode. The ode has been defined as "a strain of exalted and enthusiastic lyrical verse, directed to a fixed purpose and dealing progressively with one dignified theme." * This definition precisely fits the One Hundred and Nineteenth Psalm.

Its theme is *The Eternal Word*. Every verse in the poem, except one, contains some name or description of the law, commandments, testimonies, precepts, statutes, or judgements of Jehovah. Its enthusiasm for the Divine Righteousness never fails from beginning to end. Its fixed purpose is to kindle in other hearts the flame of devotion to the one Holy Law. It closes with a touch of magnificent pathos—a confession of personal failure and an assertion of spiritual loyalty:

* *English Odes*, selected by Edmund Gosse. Preface, page xiii.

I have gone astray like a lost sheep:
Seek thy servant:
For I do not forget thy commandments.

The Fifteenth Psalm I should call a small, didactic lyric. Its title is *The Good Citizen*. It begins with a question:

Jehovah, who shall abide in thy tabernacle?
Who shall dwell in thy holy hill?

This question is answered by the description of a man whose character corresponds to the law of God. First there is a positive sketch in three broad lines:

He that walketh uprightly,
And worketh righteousness,
And speaketh truth in his heart.

Then comes a negative characterization in a finely touched triplet:

He that backbiteth not with his tongue,
Nor doeth evil to his neighbour,
Nor taketh up a reproach against his neighbour.

This is followed by a couplet containing a strong contrast:

[78]

In whose eyes a vile person is contemned:
But he honoureth them that fear Jehovah.

Then the description goes back to the negative style again and three more touches are added to the picture:

He that sweareth to his own hurt and
changeth not,
He that putteth not out his money to usury,
Nor taketh reward against the innocent.

The poem closes with a single vigorous line, summing up the character of the good citizen and answering the question of the first verse with a new emphasis of security and permanence.

Doing these things, he shall never be moved.

The Seventy-eighth, One Hundred and Fifth, and One Hundred and Sixth Psalms are lyrical ballads. They tell the story of Israel in Egypt, and in the Wilderness, and in Canaan, with swift, stirring phrases, and with splendid flashes of imagery. Take this passage from the Seventy-eighth Psalm as an example:

He clave the rocks in the wilderness,
And gave them drink out of the great depths.

He brought streams also out of the rock,
And caused waters to run down like rivers.

And they sinned yet more against him,
Provoking the Most High in the wilderness.

They tempted God in their hearts,
Asking meat for their lust.

Yea, they spake against God:
They said, *Can God furnish a table in the wil-
    derness?*

Behold, he smote the rock that the waters
    gushed out,
And the streams overflowed;
Can he give bread also?
Can he provide flesh for his people?

Therefore Jehovah heard and was wroth:
So a fire was kindled against Jacob,
And anger also came up against Israel:
Because they believed not in God,
And trusted not in his salvation:

Though he had commanded the clouds from
    above,

[80]

And opened the doors of heaven,
And had rained down manna upon them to eat,
And had given them of the corn of heaven,
Man did eat angels' food:

He sent them meat to the full.
He caused an east wind to blow in the heaven,
And by his power he brought in the south wind.
He rained flesh also upon them as dust,
And feathered fowls like as the sand of the sea.

And he let it fall in the midst of their camp,
Round about their habitations;
So they did eat and were filled,
For he gave them their own desire.

They were not estranged from their lust:
But while the meat was yet in their mouths,
The wrath of God came upon them, and slew the
    fattest of them,
And smote down the chosen men of Israel.

The Forty-fifth Psalm is a Marriage Ode:
the Hebrew title calls it a Love Song. It
bears all the marks of having been composed for some royal wedding-feast in Jerusalem.

There are many nature lyrics among the Psalms. The Twenty-ninth is notable for its rugged realism. It is a Song of Thunder.

> The voice of the Lord breaketh the cedars:
> Yea, the Lord breaketh the cedars of Lebanon:
> He maketh them also to skip like a calf:
> Lebanon and Sirion like a young unicorn.

The One Hundred and Fourth, on the contrary, is full of calm sublimity and meditative grandeur.

> Jehovah, my God, thou art very great:
> Thou art clothed with honour and majesty:
>
> Who coverest thyself with light as with a garment;
> Who stretchest out the heavens like a curtain.

The Nineteenth is famous for its splendid comparison between "the starry heavens and the moral law."

I think that we may find also some dramatic lyrics among the Psalms—poems composed to express the feelings of an historic person, like David or Solomon, in certain well-known and striking experiences of his life. That a later writer should thus embody and express the truth dramatically through the personality of some great hero of the past, involves no falsehood. It is a mode of utterance which has been common to the literature of all lands and of all ages. Such a method of composition would certainly be no hindrance to the spirit of inspiration. The Thirty-first Psalm, for instance, is ascribed by the title to David. But there is strong reason, in the phraseology and in the spirit of the poem, to believe that it was written by the Prophet Jeremiah.

III

I T is not to be supposed that our rever-
ence for the Psalms in their moral and
religious aspects will make us put them all
on the same level poetically. There is a difference among the books of the New Testament in regard to the purity and dignity
of the Greek in which they are written.
There is a difference among St. Paul's Epis-
tles in regard to the clearness and force of
their style. There is a difference even among
the chapters of the same epistle in regard
to the beauty of thought and language. In
the First Epistle to the Corinthians, the thir-
teenth chapter is poetic, and the fourteenth
is prosaic. Why should there not be a difference in poetic quality among the Psalms?

There is a difference. The honest reader
will recognize it. It will be no harm to him
if he should have his favourites among the
poems which have been gathered from many
centuries into this great collection.

· ·

There are some, like the Twenty-seventh,

the Forty-second, the Forty-sixth, the
Fifty-first, the Sixty-third, the Ninety-first,
the Ninety-sixth, the One Hundred and
Third, the One Hundred and Seventh, the
One Hundred and Thirty-ninth, which are
among the noblest poems of the world.
Others move on a lower level, and show
the traces of effort and constraint. There
are also manifest alterations and interpola-
tions, which are not always improvements.
Dr. Perowne, who is one of the wisest and
most conservative of modern commenta-
tors, says, "Many of the Psalms have not
come down to us in their original form," *
and refers to the alterations which the Sev-
entieth makes in the Fortieth, and the
Fifty-third in the Fourteenth. The last two
verses of the Fifty-first were evidently
added by a later hand. The whole book, in
its present form, shows the marks of its
compilation and use as the Hymn-Book of
the Jewish people. Not only in the titles,
but also in the text, we can discern the work
of the compiler, critic, and adapter, sometimes wise, but occasionally otherwise.

* *The Book of Psalms.* 2 volumes, London, 1883. Volume i. page 82.

IV

THE most essential thing in the appreciation of the poetry of the Psalms is the recognition of the three great spiritual qualities which distinguish it, and are the evidences, not only of genius, but also of inspiration.

The first of these is the deep and genuine love of nature. The psalmists delight in the vision of the world, and their joy quickens their senses to read alike the larger hieroglyphs of glory written in the stars and the delicate tracings of transient beauty on leaf and flower; to hear alike the mighty roaring of the sea and the soft sweet laughter of the rustling cornfields. But in all these they see and hear the handwriting and the voice of God. It is His presence that makes the world sublime and beautiful. The direct, piercing, elevating sense of this presence simplifies, enlarges, and ennobles their style, and makes it different from other nature-poetry. They never lose themselves, like Theocritus and Wordsworth and Shelley and Tennyson, in the contemplation and description of natural beauty. They see it, but they always see beyond it. Compare, for example, a modern versified translation with the psalm itself:

> The spacious firmament on high,
> With all the blue ethereal sky
> And spangled heavens, a shining frame,
> Their Great Original proclaim.*

Addison's descriptive epithets betray a conscious effort to make a splendid picture. But the psalmist felt no need of this; a larger impulse lifted him at once into "the grand style:"

> The heavens declare the glory of God;
> And the firmament showeth his handiwork.

The second quality of the poetry of the Psalms is their passionate sense of the beauty of holiness. Keats was undoubtedly right in his suggestion that the poet must always see truth in the form of beauty. Otherwise he may be a philosopher, or a critic, or a moralist, but he is not a true poet. But we must go on from this stand-

* Joseph Addison, 1712.

point to the Platonic doctrine that the highest form of beauty is spiritual and ethical. It is the harmony of the soul with the eternal music of the Good. And the highest poets are those who, like the psalmists, are most ardently enamoured of righteousness. This fills their songs with sweetness and fire incomparable and immortal:

> The fear of the Lord is clean, enduring for ever:
> The judgments of the Lord are true and righteous altogether.
> More to be desired are they than gold, yea, than much fine gold:
> Sweeter also than honey and the honeycomb.

The third quality of the poetry of the Psalms is their intense joy in God. No lover ever poured out the longings of his heart towards his mistress more eagerly than David voiced his desire and thirst for God. No conqueror ever sang of victory more exultantly than David rejoiced in the Lord, who was his light and his salvation, the strength of his life and his portion forever.

After all, the true mission of poetry is to

increase joy. It must, indeed, be sensitive to sorrow and acquainted with grief. But it has wings given to it in order that it may bear us up into the ether of gladness.

There is no perfect joy without love. Therefore love-poetry is the best. But the highest of all love-poetry is that which celebrates, with the Psalms,

that Love which is and was
My Father and my Brother and my God.

JOY AND POWER

JOY AND POWER

If ye know these things, happy are ye if ye do them.
St. John xiii. 17.

I ASK you to think for a little while about the religion of Christ in its relation to happiness.

This is only one point in the circle of truth at the centre of which Jesus stands. But it is an important point because it marks one of the lines of power which radiate from Him. To look at it clearly and steadily is not to disregard other truths. The mariner takes the whole heavens of astronomy for granted while he shapes his course by a single star.

In the wish for happiness all men are strangely alike. In their explanations of it and in their ways of seeking it they are singularly different. Shall we think of this wish as right, or wrong; as a true star, or a will-o'-the-wisp? If it is right to wish to be happy, what are the conditions on which the fulfilment of this wish depends? These are the two questions with which I would come to

Christ, seeking instruction and guidance.

1. The desire of happiness, beyond all doubt, is a natural desire. It is the law of life itself that every being seeks and strives toward the perfection of its kind, the realization of its own specific ideal in form and function, and a true harmony with its environment. Every drop of sap in the tree flows toward foliage and fruit. Every drop of blood in the bird beats toward flight and song. In a conscious being this movement toward perfection must take a conscious form. This conscious form is happiness,— the satisfaction of the vital impulse,— the rhythm of the inward life,— the melody of a heart that has found its keynote. To say that all men long for this is simply to confess that all men are human, and that their thoughts and feelings are an essential part of their life. Virtue means a completed manhood. The joyful welfare of the soul belongs to the fulness of that ideal. Holiness is wholeness. In striving to realize the true aim of our being, we find the wish for happiness implanted in the very heart of our effort.

Now what does Christ say in regard to this natural human wish? Does He say that it is an illusion? Does He condemn and deny it? Would He have accepted Goethe's definition: "religion is renunciation"?

Surely such a notion is far from the spirit of Jesus. There is nothing of the hardness of Stoicism, the coldness of Buddhism, in Christ's gospel. It is humane, sympathetic, consoling. Unrest and weariness, the fever of passion and the chill of despair, soul-solitude and heart-trouble, are the very things that He comes to cure. He begins His great discourse with a series of beatitudes. "Blessed" is the word. "Happy" is the meaning. Nine times He rings the changes on that word, like a silver bell sounding from His fair temple on the mountain-side, calling all who long for happiness to come to Him and find rest for their souls.

Christ never asks us to give up merely for the sake of giving up, but always in order to win something better. He comes not to destroy, but to fulfil,—to fill full,—to re-plenish life with true, inward, lasting riches. His gospel is a message of satisfaction, of attainment, of felicity. Its voice is not a sigh, but a song. Its final word is a benediction, a *good-saying*. "These things have I spoken unto you, that my joy might remain in you, and that your joy might be full."

If we accept His teaching we must believe that men are not wrong in wishing for happiness, but wrong in their way of seeking it. *Earthly happiness*,—pleasure that belongs to the senses and perishes with them, —earthly happiness is a dream and a delusion. But *happiness on earth*,—spiritual joy and peace, blossoming here, fruiting hereafter,—immortal happiness, is the keynote of life in Christ.

And if we come to Him, He tells us four great secrets in regard to it.

i. It is inward, and not outward; and so it does not depend on what we have, but on what we are.

ii. It cannot be found by direct seeking, but by setting our faces toward the things from which it flows; and so we must climb the mount if we would see the vision, we must tune the instrument if we would hear the music.

iii. It is not solitary, but social; and so we can never have it without sharing it with others.

iv. It is the result of God's will for us, and not of our will for ourselves; and so we can only find it by giving our lives up, in submission and obedience, to the control of God.

> For this is peace,—to lose the lonely note
> Of self in love's celestial ordered strain:
> And this is joy,—to find one's self again
> In Him whose harmonies forever float
> Through all the spheres of song, below,
>   above,—
> For God is music, even as God is love.

This is the divine doctrine of happiness as Christ taught it by His life and with His lips. If we want to put it into a single phrase, I know not where we shall find a more perfect utterance than in the words which have been taught us in childhood,—words so strong, so noble, so cheerful, that they summon the heart of manhood like marching-music: "Man's chief end is to glorify God and enjoy Him forever."

Let us accept without reserve this teaching of our Divine Lord and Master in regard to the possibility and the duty of happiness. It is an essential element of His gospel. The atmosphere of the New Testament is not gloom, but gladness; not despondency, but hope. The man who is not glad to be a Christian is not the right kind of a Christian.

The first thing that commended the Church of Jesus to the weary and disheartened world in the early years of her triumph was her power to make her children happy,— happy in the midst of afflictions, happy in the release from the burden of guilt, happy in the sense of Divine Fatherhood and human brotherhood, happy in Christ's victory over sin and death, happy in the assurance of an endless life. At midnight in the prison, Paul and Silas sang praises, and the prisoners heard them. The lateral force of joy,— that was the power of the Church.

"Poor world," she cried, "so deep accurst,
Thou runn'st from pole to pole

To seek a draught to slake thy thirst,—
  Go seek it in thy soul."

.   .   .   .

Tears washed the trouble from her face!
  She changed into a child!
'Mid weeds and wrecks she stood,—a place
  Of ruin,—but she smiled!

Much has the Church lost of that pristine and powerful joy. The furnace of civilization has withered and hardened her. She has become anxious and troubled about many things. She has sought earthly honours, earthly powers. Richer she is than ever before, and probably better organized, and perhaps more intelligent, more learned,—but not more happy. The one note that is most often missing in Christian life, in Christian service, is the note of spontaneous joy.

Christians are not as much calmer, steadier, stronger, and more cheerful than other people as they ought to be. Some Christians are among the most depressing and worryful people in the world,—the most difficult to live with. And some, indeed, have adopted a theory of spiritual ethics which puts a special value upon unhappiness. The dark, morbid spirit which mistrusts every joyful feeling, and depreciates every cheerful virtue, and looks askance upon every happy life as if there must be something wrong about it, is a departure from the beauty of Christ's teaching to follow the dark-browed philosophy of the Orient.

The religion of Jesus tells us that cheerful piety is the best piety. There is something finer than to do right against inclination, and that is to have an inclination to do right. There is something nobler than reluctant obedience, and that is joyful obedience. The rank of virtue is not measured by its disagreeableness, but by its sweetness to the heart that loves it. The real test of character is joy. For what you rejoice in, that you love. And what you love, that you are like.

I confess frankly that I have no admiration for the phrase "disinterested benevolence," to describe the mainspring of Christian morals. I do not find it in the New Testament,—neither the words nor the thing. Interested benevolence is what I find there. To do good to others is to make life interesting and find peace for our own souls. To glorify God is to enjoy Him. That was the spirit of the first Christians. Was not St. Paul a happier man than Herod? Did not St. Peter have more joy of his life than Nero? It is said of the first disciples that they "did eat their meat with gladness and singleness of heart." Not till that pristine gladness of life returns will the Church regain her early charm for the souls of men. Every great revival of Christian power— like those which came in the times of St. Francis of Assisi and of John Wesley— has been marked and heralded by a revival of Christian joy.

If we want the Church to be mighty in power to win men, to be a source of light in the darkness, a fountain of life in the wilderness, we must remember and renew, in the spirit of Christ, the relation of religion to human happiness.

II. What, then, are the conditions upon which true happiness depends? Christ tells us in the text: *If ye know these things, happy are ye if ye do them.*

This is the blessing with a double *if*. "If

ye know,"—this is the knowledge which Christ gives to faith. "If ye do,"—this is the obedience which faith gives to Christ. Knowing and Doing,—these are the twin pillars, Jachin and Boaz, on which the house of happiness is built. The harmony of faith and life,—this is the secret of inward joy and power.

You remember when these words were spoken. Christ had knelt to wash the disciples' feet. Peter, in penitence and self-reproach, had hesitated to permit this lowly service of Divine love. But Christ answered by revealing the meaning of His act as a symbol of the cleansing of the soul from sin. He reminded the disciples of what they knew by faith,—that He was their Saviour and their Lord. By deed and by word He called up before them the great spiritual truths which had given new meaning to their life. He summoned them to live according to their knowledge, to act upon the truth which they believed.

I am sure that His words sweep out beyond that quiet upper room, beyond that beautiful incident, to embrace the whole spiritual life. I am sure that He is revealing to us the secret of happy living which lies at the very heart of His gospel when He says: *If ye know these things, happy are ye if ye do them.*

i. "If ye know,"—there is, then, a certain kind of knowledge without which we can not be happy. There are questions arising in human nature which demand an answer. If it is denied we can not help being disappointed, restless, and sad. This is the price we have to pay for being conscious, rational creatures. If we were mere plants or animals we might go on living through our appointed years in complete indifference to the origin and meaning of our existence. But within us, as human beings, there is something that cries out and rebels against such a blind life. Man is born to ask what things mean. He is possessed with the idea that there is a significance in the world beyond that which meets his senses.

John Fiske has brought out this fact very clearly in his last book, "Through Nature to God." He shows that "in the morning twilight of existence the Human Soul vaguely

[103]

reached forth toward something akin to itself, not in the realm of fleeting phenomena,
but in the Eternal Presence beyond." He
argues by the analogy of evolution, which
always presupposes a real relation between
the life and the environment to which it
adjusts itself, that this forth-reaching and
unfolding of the soul implies the everlasting reality of religion.

The argument is good. But the point
which concerns us now is simply this: The
forth-reaching, questioning soul can never
be satisfied if it touches only a dead wall in
the darkness, if its seeking meets with the
reply, "You do not know, and you never
can know, and you must not try to know."
This is agnosticism. It is only another way
of spelling unhappiness.

"Since Christianity is not true," wrote
Ernest Renan, "nothing interests me, or
appears worthy my attention." That is the
logical result of losing the knowledge of
spiritual things,—a life without real interest, without deep worth,—a life with a bro-
ken spring.

But suppose Renan is mistaken. Sup-

pose Christianity is true. Then the first
thing that makes it precious is that it an-
swers our questions, and tells us the things
that we must know in order to be happy.

Christianity is a revealing religion, a
teaching religion, a religion which conveys
to the inquiring spirit certain great and positive solutions of the problems of life. It is
not silent, nor ambiguous, nor incompre-
hensible in its utterance. It replies to our
questions with a knowledge which, though
limited, is definite and sufficient. It tells
us that this "order of nature, which con-
stitutes the world's experience, is only one
portion of the total universe." That the
ruler of both worlds, seen and unseen, is
God, a Spirit, and the Father of our spirits.
That He is not distant from us nor indif-
ferent to us, but that He has given His
eternal Son Jesus Christ to be our Saviour.
That His Spirit is ever present with us to
help us in our conflicts with evil, in our efforts toward goodness. That He is making
all things work together for good to those
that love Him. That through the sacrifice
of Christ every one who will may obtain the

forgiveness of sins and everlasting peace.
That through the resurrection of Christ all
who love Him and their fellow-men shall obtain the victory over death and live forever.

Now these are doctrines. And it is just
because Christianity contains such doctrines that it satisfies the need of man.

"The first and the most essential condition of true happiness," writes Professor
Carl Hilty, the eminent Swiss jurist, "is a
firm faith in the moral order of the world.
What is the happy life? It is a life of conscious harmony with this Divine order of
the world, a sense, that is to say, of God's
companionship. And wherein is the pro-
foundest unhappiness? It is in the sense of
remoteness from God, issuing into incur-
able restlessness of heart, and finally into
incapacity to make one's life fruitful or ef-
fective."

What shall we say, then, of the proposal
to adapt Christianity to the needs of the
world to-day by eliminating or ignoring its
characteristic doctrines? You might as well
propose to fit a ship for service by taking
out its compass and its charts and cutting

off its rudder. Make Christianity silent in regard to these great questions of spiritual existence, and you destroy its power to satisfy the heart.

What would the life of Christ mean if these deep truths on which He rested and from which He drew His strength, were uncertain or illusory? It would be the most pathetic, mournful, heart-breaking of all phantoms.

What consoling, cheering power would be left in the words of Jesus if His doctrine were blotted out and His precept left to stand alone? Try the experiment, if it may be done without irreverence: read His familiar discourses in the shadow of agnosticism.

'Blessed are the poor in spirit, for theirs is a hopeless poverty. Blessed are the pure in heart, for they know not whether they shall see God. Blessed are ye when men shall revile you and persecute you, for ye have no promise of a heavenly reward.

'Enter into thy closet, and when thou hast shut the door, keep silence, for thou canst not tell whether there is One to hear

[107]

thy voice in secret. Take no thought for the morrow, for thou knowest not whether there is a Father who careth for thee.

'God is unknown, and they that worship Him must worship Him in ignorance and doubt. No man hath ascended up into heaven, neither hath any man come down from heaven, for the Son of Man hath never been in heaven. That which is born of the flesh is flesh, and that which is born of the spirit is a dream. Man shall not live by bread alone, neither shall he listen for any word from the mouth of God. I proceeded forth and came from darkness, I came of myself, I know not who sent me. My sheep hear my voice, and I know them, and they follow me, but I can not give unto them eternal life, for they shall perish and death shall pluck them out of my hand. Let not your heart be troubled; ye believe not in God, ye need not believe in me. Keep my commandments, and I will not pray for you, and ye shall abide without a Comforter. In the world ye shall have tribulation, but be of good cheer, for ye know not whether there is a world to come. I came forth from darkness into the world, and again I leave the world and return to darkness. Peace I leave with you. If ye loved me ye would rejoice because I said, I go into darkness, and where I am there shall ye be also.'

Is it conceivable that any suffering, sorrowing human soul should be comforted and strengthened by such a message as this? Could it possibly be called a gospel, glad tidings of great joy to all people?

And yet what has been omitted here from the words of Christ? Nothing but what men call doctrines: the personality of God, the divinity of Christ, the Atonement, the presence and power of the Holy Spirit, the sovereignty of the Heavenly Father, the truth of the divine revelation, the reality of the heavenly world, the assurance of immortal life. But it is just from these doctrines that the teaching of Jesus draws its peculiar power to comfort and inspire. They are the rays of light which disperse the gloom of uncertainty. They are the tones of celestial music which fill the heart of man with good cheer.

[109]

Let us never imagine that we can strengthen Christianity by leaving out the great doctrines which have given it life and power. Faith is not a mere matter of feeling. It is the acceptance of truth, positive, unchanging, revealed truth, in regard to God and the world, Christ and the soul, duty and immortality. The first appeal to faith lies in the clearness and vividness, the simplicity and joy, with which this truth is presented.

There has not been too much preaching of doctrine in this age—there has been too little. And what there has been, has been too dull and cold and formal, too vague and misty, too wavering and uncertain.

What the world wants and waits for to-day is a strong, true, vital preaching of doctrine. The Church must realize anew the precious value of the truths which Christ has given her. She must not conceal them or cast them away; she must bring them out into the light, press them home upon the minds and hearts of men. She must simplify her statement of them, so that men can understand what they mean. She must not be content with repeating them in the language of past centuries. She must translate them into the language of to-day. First century texts will never wear out because they are inspired. But seventeenth century sermons grow obsolete because they are not inspired. Texts from the Word of God, preaching in the words of living men,—that is what we need.

We must think about the doctrines of Christianity more earnestly and profoundly. We must renew our Christian evidences, as an army fits itself with new weapons. The old-fashioned form of the "argument from design in nature" has gone out with the old-fashioned books of science which it used. But there is a new and more wonderful proof of God's presence in the world,—the argument from moral ends in evolution. Every real advance of science makes the intelligent order of the universe more sublimely clear. Every century of human experience confirms the Divine claims and adds to the Divine triumphs of Jesus Christ. Social progress has followed to a hair's breadth the lines of His gospel; and He

lays His hand to-day with heavenly wisdom on the social wants that still trouble
us, "the social lies that warp us from the
living truth." Christ's view of life and the
world is as full of sweet reasonableness now
as it was in the first century. Every moral
step that man has taken upward has brought
a wider, clearer vision of his need of such
a religion as that which Christ teaches.

Let not the Church falter and blush for
her doctrines. Let her not turn and go down
the hill of knowledge to defend her position in the valley of ignorance. Let her go
up the hill, welcoming every wider outlook,
rejoicing in every new discovery, gathering
fresh evidences of the truths which man
must believe concerning God and new mo-
tives to the duties which God requires of
man.

But in doing this we must put the emphasis of our preaching to-day where it belongs, where Christ puts it, on the doctrines
that are most important to human life and
happiness. We can afford to let the fine
metaphysical distinctions of theology rest for
a while, and throw all our force on the cen-

tral, fundamental truths which give stead-
iness and courage and cheer to the heart
of man. I will not admit that it makes no
difference to a man of this age whether or
not he believes in the personal God and
the Divine Christ. If he really believes, it
makes all the difference between spiritual
strength and spiritual weakness, between
optimism and pessimism. I will not admit
that it makes no difference to a learned scho-
lar or a simple labourer to-day whether he
accepts or ignores the doctrine of the atonement, the doctrine of personal immortality.
If he knows that Christ died for him, that
there is a future beyond the grave, it makes
all the difference between despair and hope,
between misery and consolation, between
the helpless frailty of a being that is puffed
out like a candle, and the joyful power of
an endless life.

My brethren, we must work and pray
for a true revival of Christian doctrine in
our age. We must deepen our own hold
upon the truths which Christ has taught
us. We must preach them more simply,
more confidently, more reasonably, more

earnestly. We must draw from them the happiness and the help, the comfort and the inspiration, that they have to give to the souls of men. But most of all, we must keep them in close and living touch with the problems of daily duty and experience. For no doctrine, however high, however true, can make men happy until it is translated into life.

ii. Here is the second *if*, on which the power of religion to confer happiness depends: *If ye know, happy are ye if ye do these things*.

Between the knowing and the doing there is a deep gulf. Into that abyss the happiness of many a man slips, and is lost. There is no peace, no real and lasting felicity, for a human life until the gulf is closed, and the continent of conduct meets the continent of creed, edge to edge, lip to lip, firmly joined forever.

It is not a blessing to know the things that Christ teaches, and then go on living as if they were false or doubtful. It is a trouble, a torment, a secret misery. To know that God is our Father, and yet to withhold our love and service from Him; to know that Christ died for us, and yet to deny Him and refuse to follow Him; to know that there is an immortal life, and yet to waste and lose our souls in the pursuit of sensual pleasure and such small portion of the world as we may hope to gain,— surely that is the deepest of all unhappiness.

But the right kind of knowing carries in its heart the doing of the truth. And the right kind of doing leads to a fuller and happier knowing. "If any man will do God's will," declares Christ, "he shall know of the doctrine."

Let a man take the truth of the Divine Fatherhood and begin to conform his life to its meaning. Let him give up his anxious worryings, his murmurings, his complainings, and trust himself completely to his Father's care. Let him do his work from day to day as well as he can and leave the results to God. Let him come to his Father every day and confess his faults and ask for help and guidance. Let him try to obey and please God for love's sake. Let him take refuge from the trials and confusions and misunderstandings of the world, from the wrath of men and the strife of tongues, in the secret of his Father's presence. Surely if he learns the truth thus, by doing it, he will find happiness.

Or take the truth of immortality. Let a man live now in the light of the knowledge that he is to live forever. How it will deepen and strengthen the meaning of his existence, lift him above petty cares and ambitions, and make the things that are worth while precious to his heart! Let him really set his affections on the spiritual side of life, let him endure afflictions patiently because he knows that they are but for a moment, let him think more of the soul than of the body, let him do good to his fellow-men in order to make them sharers of his immortal hope, let him purify his love and friendship that they may be fit for the heavenly life. Surely the man who does these things will be happy. It will be with him as with Lazarus, in Robert Browning's poem, "The Epistle of Karshish." Others will look at him with wonder and say:

Whence has the man the balm that brightens
    all?
This grown man eyes the world now like a
    child.

Yes, my brethren, this is the sure result of
following out the doctrines of Christ in action, of living the truths that He teaches,
—a simple life, a childlike life, a happy
life. And this also the Church needs to-day,
as well as a true revival of doctrine.

A revival of simplicity, a revival of sin-
cerity, a revival of work: this will restore
unto us the joy of salvation. And with the
joy of salvation will come a renewal and
expansion of power.

The inconsistency of Christians is the
stronghold of unbelief. The lack of vital
joy in the Church is the chief cause of indifference in the world. The feeble energy,
the faltering and reluctant spirit, the weariness in well-doing with which too many
believers impoverish and sadden their own
hearts, make other men question the reality
and value of religion and turn away from
it in cool neglect.

[117]

What, then, is the duty of the Church? What must she do to win the confidence of the world? What is the best way for her to "prove her doctrine all divine"?

First, she must increase her labours in the love of men; second, she must practice the simple life, deepening her trust in God.

Suppose that a fresh flood of energy, brave, cheerful, joyous energy, should be poured into all the forms of Christian work. Suppose that Foreign Missions and Home Missions should no longer have to plead and beg for support, but that plenty of money should come flowing in to send out every missionary that wants to go, and that plenty of the strongest and best young men should dedicate their lives to the ministry of Christ, and that every household where His gospel is believed should find its highest honour and its greatest joy in helping to extend His kingdom.

And then suppose that the Christian life, in its daily manifestation, should come to be marked and known by simplicity and happiness. Suppose that the followers of Jesus should really escape from bondage to

[118]

the evil spirits of avarice and luxury which
infect and torment so much of our compli-
cated, tangled, artificial, modern life. Suppose that instead of increasing their wants
and their desires, instead of loading themselves down on life's journey with so many
bags and parcels and boxes of superfluous
luggage and bric-à-brac that they are forced
to sit down by the roadside and gasp for
breath, instead of wearing themselves out
in the dusty ways of ostentation and vain
show or embittering their hearts because
they can not succeed in getting into the
weary race of wealth and fashion,—suppose
instead of all this, they should turn to quiet
ways, lowly pleasures, pure and simple joys,
"plain living and high thinking." Suppose
they should truly find and show their happiness in the knowledge that God loves
them and Christ died for them and heaven
is sure, and so set their hearts free to rejoice in life's common mercies, the light of
the sun, the blue of the sky, the splendour
of the sea, the peace of the everlasting hills,
the song of birds, the sweetness of flowers,
the wholesome savour of good food, the

delights of action and motion, the refreshment of sleep, the charm of music, the blessings of human love and friendship,— rejoice in all these without fear or misgiving, because they come from God and because Christ has sanctified them all by His presence and touch.

Suppose, I say, that such a revival of the joy of living in Christ and working for Christ should silently sweep over the Church in the Twentieth Century. What would happen? Great would be the peace of her children. Greater still would be their power.

This is the message which I have to bring to you, my brethren, in this General Assembly of the Presbyterian Church. You may wonder that it is not more distinctive, more ecclesiastical, more specially adapted to the peculiarities of our own denomination. You may think that it is a message which could just as well be brought to any other Church on any other occasion. With all my heart I hope that is true. The things that I care for most in our Church are not those which divide us from other

Christians, but those which unite us to them. The things that I love most in Christianity are those which give it power to save and satisfy, to console and cheer, to inspire and bless, human hearts and lives. The thing that I desire most for Presbyterianism is that it should prove its mission and extend its influence in the world by making men happy in the knowing and the doing of the things which Christ teaches.

The Church that the Twentieth Century will hear most gladly and honour most sincerely will have two marks. It will be the Church that teaches most clearly and strongly the truths that Jesus taught. It will be the Church that finds most happiness in living the simple life and doing good in the world.

THE BATTLE OF LIFE

THE BATTLE OF LIFE

Overcome evil with good. Romans xii. 21.

THE Battle of Life is an ancient phrase consecrated by use in Commencement Orations without number. Two modern expressions have taken their place beside it in our own day,—the Strenuous Life and the Simple Life.

Each of these phrases has its own significance and value. It is when they are overemphasized and driven to extremes that they lose their truth and become catchwords of folly. The simple life which blandly ignores all care and conflict soon becomes flabby and invertebrate, sentimental and gelatinous. The strenuous life which does everything with set jaws and clenched fists and fierce effort soon becomes strained and violent, a prolonged nervous spasm.

Somewhere between these two extremes must lie the golden mean,—a life that has strength and simplicity, courage and calm, power and peace. But how can we find this golden line and live along it? Some truth there must be in the old phrase which speaks of life as a battle. No conflict, no character. Without strife, a weak life. But what is the real meaning of the battle? What is the vital issue at stake? What are the things worth fighting for? In what spirit, with what weapons, are we to take our part in the warfare?

There is an answer to these questions in the text: *Overcome evil with good.* The man who knows this text by heart, knows the secret of a life that is both strenuous and simple. For here we find the three things that we need most: a call to the real battle of life; a plan for the right campaign; and a promise of final victory.

1. Every man, like the knight in the old legend, is born on a field of battle. But the warfare is not carnal, it is spiritual. Not the East against the West, the North against the South, the "Haves" against the "Have-nots;" but the evil against the good,—that is the real conflict of life.

The attempt to deny or ignore this conflict has been the stock in trade of every false doctrine that has befogged and be-

wildered the world since the days of Eden.
The fairy tale that the old serpent told to
Eve is a poetic symbol of the lie fundamental,— the theory that sin does not
mean death, because it has no real existence
and makes no real difference. This ancient
falsehood has an infinite wardrobe of dis-
guises.

You will find it pranked out in philo-
sophic garb in the doctrines of those who
teach that all things are linked together by
necessity of nature or Divine will, and that
nothing could ever have happened otherwise than just as it has come to pass. Such
a theory of the universe blots out all difference between good and evil except in name.
It leaves the fence-posts standing, but it
takes away the rails, and throws everything
into one field of the inevitable.

You will find the same falsehood in a
more crude form in the popular teachings
of what men call "the spirit of the age,"
the secular spirit. According to these doctrines the problem of civilization is merely
a problem of ways and means. If society
were better organized, if wealth were more

equally distributed, if laws were changed, or perhaps abolished, all would be well. If everybody had a full dinner-pail, nobody need care about an empty heart. Human misery the secular spirit recognizes, but it absolutely ignores the fact that nine-tenths of human misery comes from human sin.

You will find the same falsehood disguised in sentimental costume in the very modern comedy of Christian Science, which dresses the denial of evil in pastoral garb of white frock and pink ribbons, like an innocent shepherdess among her lambs. "Evil is nothing," says this wonderful Science. "It does not really exist. It is an illusion of mortal mind. Shut your eyes and it will vanish."

Yes, but open your eyes again and you will see it in the same place, in the same form, doing the same work. A most persistent nothing, a most powerful nothing! Not the shadow cast by the good, but the cloud that hides the sun and casts the shadow. Not the "silence implying sound," but the discord breaking the harmony. Evil is as real as the fire that burns you, as the flood that drowns you. Evil is as real as the typhoid germ that you can put under a microscope and see it squirm and grow. Evil is negative,—yes, but it is a real negative,—as real as darkness, as real as death.

There are two things in every human heart which bear witness to the existence and reality of evil: first, our judgements of regret, and second, our judgements of condemnation.

How often we say to ourselves, "Would that this had not come to pass!" How often we feel in regard to our own actions, "Would that I had done differently!" This is the judgement of regret; and it is a silent witness of the heart to the conviction that some things are not inevitable. It is the confession that a battle has been lost which might have been won. It is the acknowledgement that things which are, but are not right, need not have been, if we and our fellow-men had seen more clearly and followed more faithfully the guiding star of the good.

And then, out of the judgement of regret,

springs the deeper judgement of condemnation. If the failure in duty was not inevitable, then it was base. The false word, the unjust deed, the foul action, seen as a surrender to evil, appears hateful and guilty. It deserves the indignation and the shame which attach to all treason. And the spirit which lies behind all these forms of disloyalty to the good,—the spirit which issues in selfishness and sensuality, cruelty and lust, intemperance and covetousness,—this animating spirit of evil which works against the Divine will and mars the peace and order of the universe is the great Adversary against whom we must fight for our own lives and the life of the world.

All around us lies his dark, secret kingdom, tempting, threatening, assaulting the soul. To ignore it, is to walk blindfold among snares and pitfalls. Try if you will to shut it out, by wrapping your heart in dreams of beauty and joy, living in the fair regions of art or philosophy, reading only the books which speak of evil as if it did not exist or were only another form of goodness. Soon you will be shaken out of the dream into the reality. You will come into contact with evil so close, so loathsome, that you can not deny it. You will see that it has its soldiers, its servants, its emissaries, as ardent and enthusiastic in its cause as if they were serving the noblest of masters. It inspires literature and supports newspapers; now intelligent and cultured, drawing the arts into its service; now coarse and vulgar, with pictures that shock the taste as much as they debase the conscience. It wins adherents and turns them into advocates. It organizes the dealers in drunkenness and debauchery into powerful societies for mutual protection. It creates lobbies and controls legislatures. It corrupts the government of great cities and rots out the social life of small towns. Even when its outward manifestations are repressed and its grosser forms resisted, it steals its way into men's hearts, eating out the roots of human trust and brotherhood and kindness, and filling the air with gossip and spite, envy, malice and all uncharitableness.

I am glad that since we have to live in a world where evil exists, we have a religion which does not bandage our eyes. The first thing that we need to have religion do for us is to teach us to face the facts. No man can come into touch with the Divine personality of Jesus Christ, no man can listen to His teaching, without feeling that the distinction between good and evil to Him is vital and everlasting. The choice between them is to Him the great choice. The conflict between them is to Him the great conflict. Evil is the one thing that God has never willed. Good is the one thing that He wills forever. Evil is first and last a rebellion against His will. He is altogether on the side of good. Much that is, is contrary to His will. There is a mighty strife going on, a battle with eternal issues, but not an eternal battle. The evil that is against Him shall be cast out and shall perish. The good that overcomes the evil shall live forever. And those who yield their lives to God and receive His righteousness in Christ are made partakers of everlasting life.

This is the teaching of Jesus; and I thank God for the honesty and virility of His religion which makes us face the facts and calls us to take a man's part in the real battle of life.

11. But what is the plan of campaign which Christianity sets before us? In what spirit and with what weapons are we to enter the great conflict against the evil that is in the world?

The natural feeling of the heart in the presence of evil is wrath, and the natural weapon of wrath is force. To punish crime, to avenge wrong, to put down wickedness with a strong hand,—that is the first impulse of every one who has the instincts of manhood.

And as this is natural, so it is, also, within a certain sphere needful, and to a certain extent useful. Armies and navies exist, at least in theory, to prevent injustice among nations. Laws are made to punish wrong-doers. Courts, police-forces, and prisons are maintained to suppress evil with power.

But while we recognize this method of dealing with evil as useful to a certain extent and necessary within a certain sphere, we must remember that it has its strict limitations.

[133]

First, it belongs to the state and not to the individual. When the private man assumes to punish evil with force he sanctions lynch-law, which is a terror to the innocent as well as to the guilty. Then we have the blood-feud and the vendetta, mob-rule and anarchy.

Second, the suppression of evil by force is only a temporary relief, a protection for the moment. It does not touch the root of the matter. You send the murderer out of the world by a regulated flash of lightning. But you do not send murder out of the world. To do that you must reach and change the heart of Cain. You put the thief in prison, but when he comes out he will be ready to steal again, unless you can purify his conscience and control his will. You assault and overthrow some system of misgovernment, and "turn the rascals out." But unless you have something better to substitute, all you have done is to make room for a new set of rascals,—a new swarm of mosquitoes with fresh appetites and larger capacities.

Third, the method of fighting evil with

force on its own ground often has a bad
effect on those who follow it. Wrestle with
a chimney-sweep and you will need a bath.
Throw back the mud that is thrown at
you, and you will have dirty hands. Answer
Shimei when he curses you and you will
echo his profanity. Many a man has entered
a crusade against intemperance and proved
himself as intemperate in his language as
other men are in their potations. Many a
man has attacked a bad cause with righteous
indignation and ended in a personal squab-
ble with most unrighteous anger.

No, my brother-men, the best way to
fight against evil is not to meet it on its
own ground with its own weapons. There
is a nobler method of warfare, a divine plan
of campaign given to us in the religion of
Christ. *Overcome evil with good*. This is the
secret of the battle of life.

Evil is potent not so much because it
has command of money and the "big bat-
talions," but because it has control of the
hearts of men. It spreads because human
hearts are lying fallow and ready to welcome
the seeds of all kinds of weeds. It persists

because too much of what we call virtue is
negative, and selfish, and frost-bound,—
cold-storage virtue,—the poor piety which
terminates in a trembling anxiety to save
our own souls.

The way to counteract and conquer evil
in the world is to give our own hearts to
the dominion of good, and work the works
of God while it is day. The strongest of
all obstacles to the advance of evil is a clean
and generous man, doing his duty from
day to day, and winning others, by his
cheerful fidelity, to serve the same Master.
Diseases are not the only things that are
contagious. Courage is contagious. Kindness is contagious. Manly integrity is contagious. All the positive virtues, with red
blood in their veins, are contagious. The
heaviest blow that you can strike at the
kingdom of evil is just to follow the advice
which the dying Sir Walter Scott gave to
his son-in-law, Lockhart: "Be a good man."
And if you want to know how, there is but
one perfect and supreme example,—the life
of Him who not only did no evil, but went
about doing good.

Now take that thought of fighting evil with good and apply it to our world and to ourselves.

Here are monstrous evils and vices in society. Let intemperance be the type of them all, because so many of the others are its children. Drunkenness ruins more homes and wrecks more lives than war. How shall we oppose it? I do not say that we shall not pass resolutions and make laws against it. But I do say that we can never really conquer the evil in this way. I hold with Phillips Brooks that "all prohibitory measures are negative. That they have their uses no one can doubt. That they have their limits is just as clear."

The stronghold of intemperance lies in the vacancy and despair of men's minds. The way to attack it is to make the sober life beautiful and happy and full of interest. Teach your boys how to work, how to read, how to play, you fathers, before you send them to college, if you want to guard them against the temptations of strong drink and the many shames and sorrows that go with it. Make the life of your community cheer-

ful and pleasant and interesting, you re-
formers, provide men with recreation which
will not harm them, if you want to take
away the power of the gilded saloon and
the grimy boozing-ken. Parks and play-
grounds, libraries and music-rooms, clean
homes and cheerful churches,—these are
the efficient foes of intemperance. And the
same thing is true of gambling and lubri-
city and all the other vices which drag men
down by the lower side of their nature because the higher side has nothing to cling
to, nothing to sustain it and hold it up.

What are you going to do, my brother-
men, for this higher side of human life?
What contribution are you going to make
of your strength, your time, your influence,
your money, your self, to make a cleaner,
fuller, happier, larger, nobler life possible
for some of your fellow-men? I do not ask
how you are going to do it. You may do
it in business, in the law, in medicine, in
the ministry, in teaching, in literature. But
this is the question: What are you going to
give personally to make the human life of
the place where you do your work, purer,

stronger, brighter, better, and more worth living? That will be your best part in the warfare against vice and crime.

The positive method is the only efficient way to combat intellectual error and spiritual evil. False doctrines are never argued out of the world. They are pushed back by the incoming of the truth as the darkness is pushed back by the dawn. Phillips Brooks was right. It is not worth while to cross the street to break a man's idol. It is worth while to cross the ocean to tell him about God. The skilful fencer who attacks your doubts and drives you from corner to corner of unbelief and leaves you at last in doubt whether you doubt or not, does you a certain service. He gives you exercise, takes the conceit out of you. But the man who lays hold of the real faith that is hidden underneath your doubt,—the silent longing for God and goodness, the secret attraction that draws your heart toward Jesus Christ as the only one who has the words of everlasting life,—the man who takes hold of this buried faith and quickens it and makes you dare to try to live by it,

[139]

—ah, that is the man who helps you indeed. My brothers, if any of you are going to be preachers remember this: What we men need is not so much an answer to our doubts, as more nourishment for our faith.

The positive method is the only way of victory in our struggle with the evil that dwells in our own nature and besets our own hearts. The reason why many men fail is because they thrust the vice out and then forget to lay hold on the virtue. They evict the unclean spirit and leave a vacant house. To cease to do evil is important, but to learn to do good is far more important. Reformation never saved a man. Transformation is the only way. And to be transformed, a man must welcome the Spirit of Good, the Holy Spirit, into his heart, and work with Him every day, doing the will of God.

There are two ways of fighting fever. One is to dose the sick people with quinine and keep the fever down. The other is to drain the marshes, and purify the water, and cleanse the houses, and drive the fever out. Try negative, repressive religion, and you may live, but you will be an invalid. Try positive, vital religion, and you will be well.

There is an absorption of good that guards the soul against the infection of evil. There is a life of fellowship with Christ that can pass through the furnace of the world without the smell of fire on its garments,— a life that is full of interest as His was, being ever about His Father's business; a life that is free and generous and blessed, as His was, being spent in doing good, and refreshed by the sense of God's presence and approval.

Last summer I saw two streams emptying into the sea. One was a sluggish, niggardly rivulet, in a wide, fat, muddy bed; and every day the tide came in and drowned out that poor little stream, and filled it with bitter brine. The other was a vigorous, joyful, brimming mountain-river, fed from unfailing springs among the hills; and all the time it swept the salt water back before it and kept itself pure and sweet; and when the tide came in, it only made the fresh water rise higher and gather new strength by the delay; and ever the living stream poured forth into the ocean its tribute of living water, — the symbol of that influence which keeps the ocean of life from turning into a Dead Sea of wickedness.

My brother-men, will you take that living stream as a type of your life in the world? The question for you is not what you are going to get out of the world, but what you are going to give to the world. The only way to meet and overcome the inflowing tide of evil is to roll against it the outflowing river of good.

My prayer for you is that you may receive from Christ not only the watchword of this nobler life, but also the power to fulfil it.

THE GOOD OLD WAY

THE GOOD OLD WAY

Stand ye in the ways, and see; and ask for the old paths, where is the good way; and walk therein, and ye shall find rest for your souls. Jeremiah vi. 16.

THIS advice was given to people who were in peril and perplexity. The kingdom of Judah was threatened with destruction, which could be averted only by wise and prompt action. But the trouble was to decide in which direction that action should be taken. The nation was divided into loud parties, and these parties into noisy wings. Every man had a theory of his own, or a variation of some other man's theory.

Some favoured an alliance with the East; some preferred the friendship of the West; others, a course of diplomatic dalliance; a few stood out for honest independence. Some said that what the country needed was an increase of wealth; some held that a splendid and luxurious court, like that of Pharaoh or Nebuchadnezzar, would bring prosperity; others maintained that the troubles of the land could be healed only by a return to "simpler manners, purer laws." Among the nobility and their followers all kinds of novelties in the worship of idols were in fashion and new gods were imported every season. The philosophers cultivated a discreet indifference to all religious questions. The prophets taught that the only salvation for the nation lay in the putting away of idolatry and the revival of faith in the living and true God.

Judah was like a man standing at the cross-roads, on a stormy night, with all the guide-posts blown down. Meantime the Babylonian foe was closing in around Jerusalem, and it was necessary to do something, or die.

The liberty of choice was an embarrassment. The minds of men alternated between that rash haste which is ready to follow any leader who makes noise enough, and that skeptical spirit which doubts whether any line of action can be right because so many lines are open. Into this atmosphere of fever and fog came the word of the prophet. Let us consider what it means.

[146]

Stand ye in the ways and see—that means deliberation. When you are at a junction it is no time to shut your eyes and run at full speed. Where there are so many ways some of them are likely to be wrong. A turning-point is the place for prudence and fore-thought.

Ask for the old paths, what is the good way —that means guidance. No man is forced to face the problems of life alone. Other men have tried the different ways. Peace, prosperity, victory have been won by the nation in former times. Inquire of the past how these blessings were secured. Look for the path which has already led to safety and happiness. Let history teach you which among all these crossing ways is the best to follow.

And walk therein—that means action. When you have deliberated, when you have seen the guiding light upon the way of security and peace, then go ahead. Prudence is worthless unless you put it into practice. When in doubt do nothing; but as long as you do nothing you will be in doubt. Never man or nation was saved by inaction. The only way out of danger is the way into work.

[147]

Gird up your loins, trembling Judah, and push along your chosen path, steadily, bravely, strenuously, until you come to your promised rest.

Now I am sure this was good counsel that the prophet gave to his people in the days of perplexity. It would have been well for them if they had followed it. I am sure it is also good counsel for us, a word of God to steady us and stimulate us amid life's confusions. Let me make it a personal message to you.

Stand in the ways; Ask for the good way; Walk therein, — Deliberation, Guidance, Action. Will you take these words with you, and try to make them a vital influence in your life?

1. First, I ask you to *stand in the ways, and see.* I do not mean to say that you have not already been doing this to a certain extent. The great world is crossed by human footsteps which make paths leading in all directions. Men travel through on different ways; and I suppose some of you have noticed the fact, and thought a little about it.

There is the way of sensuality. Those

who walk in it take appetite as their guide. Their main object in life is to gratify their physical desires. Some of them are delicate, and some of them are coarse. That is a matter of temperament. But all of them are hungry. That is a matter of principle. Whether they grub in the mire for their food like swine, or browse daintily upon the tree-tops like the giraffe, the question of life for those who follow this way is the same. "How much can we hold? How can we obtain the most pleasure for these five senses of ours before they wear out?" And the watchword of their journey is, "Let us eat and drink and be merry, for we do not expect to die to-morrow."

There is the way of avarice. Those who follow it make haste to be rich. The almighty dollar rolls before them along the road, and they chase it. Some of them plod patiently along the highway of toil. Others are always leaping fences and trying to find short cuts to wealth. But they are alike in this: whatever they do by way of avocation, the real vocation of their life is to make money. If they fail, they are hard and bit-

[149]

ter; if they succeed they are hard and proud. But they all bow down to the golden calf, and their motto is, "Lay up for yourselves treasures upon earth."

There is the way of social ambition. Those who walk in it have their eyes fixed on various prizes, such as titles of honour, public office, large acquaintance with prosperous people, the reputation of leading the fashion. But the real satisfaction that they get out of it all is simply the feeling of notoriety, the sense of belonging to a circle to which ordinary people are not admitted and to whose doings the world, just for this reason, pays envious attention. This way is less like a road than like a ladder. Most of the people who are on it are "climbers."

There are other ways, less clearly marked, more difficult to trace,—the way of moral indifference, the way of intellectual pride, the way of hypocrisy, the way of indecision. This last is not a single road: it is a network of sheep-tracks, crossing and recrossing the great highways, leading in every direction, and ending nowhere. The men who wander in these aimless paths go up

and down through the world, changing their
purposes, following one another blindly,
forever travelling, but never arriving at the
goal of their journey.

Through all this tangle there runs another way,—the path of faith and duty.
Those who walk in it believe that life has
a meaning,—the fulfilment of God's will;
and a goal,—the attainment of perfect harmony with Him. They try to make the best
of themselves in soul and body by training
and discipline. They endeavour to put their
talents to the noblest use in the service of
their fellow-men, and to unfold their faculties to the highest joy and power in the life
of the Spirit. They seek an education to
fit them for work, and they do their work
well because it is a part of their education.
They respect their consciences, and cherish
their ideals. They put forth an honest effort
to be good and to do good and to make the
world better. They often stumble. They
sometimes fall. But, take their life from end
to end, it is a faithful attempt to walk in
"the way of righteousness, which is the way
of peace."

[151]

Such are some of the ways that lead through the world. And they are all open to us. We can travel by the road that pleases us. Heredity gives us our outfit. Environment supplies our company. But when we come to the cross-roads, the question is, "Boy, which way will you ride?"

Deliberation is necessary, unless we wish to play a fool's part. No amount of energy will take the place of thought. A strenuous life, with its eyes shut, is a kind of wild insanity. A drifting life, with its eyes open, is a kind of mild idiocy.

The real question is, "How will you live? After what rule and pattern? Along what way? Toward what end?"

Will you let chance answer that question for you? Will you let yourself be led blindfold by the first guide that offers, or run stupidly after the crowd without asking whither they are going? You would not act so in regard to the shortest earthly journey. You would not rush into the railway station and jump aboard of the first train you saw, without looking at the signboards. Surely if there is anything in regard to which we

[152]

need to exercise deliberation, it is the choice of the way that we are to take through the world. You have thought a good deal about what business, what profession you are to follow. Think more deeply, I beg you, about how you are to follow it and what you are to follow it for. *Stand in the ways, and see.*

ii. Second, I earnestly advise you to *ask for the old paths, where is the good way.*

I do not regard this as a mere counsel of conservatism, an unqualified commendation of antiquity. True, it implies that the good way will not be a new discovery, a track that you and I strike out for ourselves. Among the paths of conduct, that which is entirely original is likely to be false, and that which is true is likely to have some footprints on it. When a man comes to us with a scheme of life which he has made all by himself, we may safely say to him, as the old composer said to the young musician who brought him a symphony of the future, "It is both new and beautiful; but that which is new is not beautiful, and that which is beautiful is not new."

[153]

But this is by no means the same as saying that everything ancient is therefore beautiful and true, or that all the old ways are good. The very point of the text is that we must discriminate among antiquities,— a thing as necessary in old chairs and old books as in old ways.

Evil is almost, if not quite, as ancient as good. Folly and wisdom, among men at least, are twins, and we can not distinguish between them by the gray hairs. Adam's way was old enough; and so was the way of Cain, and of Noah's vile son, and of Lot's lewd daughters, and of Balaam, and of Jezebel, and of Manasseh. Judas Iscariot was as old as St. John. Ananias and Sapphira were of the same age with St. Peter and St. Paul.

What we are to ask for is not simply the old way, but that one among the old ways which has been tested and tried and proved to be the good way. The Spirit of Wisdom tells us that we are not to work this way out by logarithms, or evolve it from our own inner consciousness, but to learn what it is by looking at the lives of other men and marking the lessons which they teach us. Experience has been compared to the stern-light of a ship which shines only on the road that has been traversed. But the stern-light of a ship that sails before you is a head-light to you.

You do not need to try everything for yourself in order to understand what it means. The writer of Ecclesiastes tells us that he gave his heart to know madness and folly; and that it was all vanity and vexation of spirit. It will be a wise economy for us to accept his lesson without paying his tuition-fee over again.

It is perfectly safe for a man to take it as a fact that fire burns, without putting his hand into the flame. He does not need to try perilous experiments with his own soul in order to make sure that lust defiles, that avarice hardens, that frivolity empties, that selfishness cankers the heart. He may understand the end of the way of sensuality by looking at any old pleasure-seeker,

Gray, and gap-toothed, and lean as death,

mumbling the dainties that he can no longer

[155]

enjoy, and glowering with bleared eyes at the indulgences which now mock him even while they tempt him. The goal of the path of covetousness may be discerned in the face of any old money-worshipper, keeping guard over his piles of wealth like a surly watch-dog; or, if perchance he has failed, haunting the places where fortune has deceived him, like an unquiet ghost.

Inquire and learn; consider and discern. There need be no doubt about the direction of life's various ways.

Which are the nations that have been most peaceful and noble and truly prosperous? Those that have followed pride and luxury and idolatry? or those that have cherished sobriety and justice, and acknowledged the Divine law of righteousness?

Which are the families that have been most serene and pure and truly fortunate? Those in which there has been no discipline, no restraint, no common faith, no mutual love? or those in which sincere religion has swayed life to its stern and gracious laws, those in which parents and children have walked together to the House of God, and

knelt together at His altar, and rejoiced
together in His service?

I tell you, my brother-men, it has become too much the fashion in these latter
days to sneer and jeer at the old-fashioned
ways of the old-fashioned American household. Something too much of iron there
may have been in the Puritan's temper;
something too little of sunlight may have
come in through the narrow windows of
his house. But that house had foundations,
and the virile virtues lived in it. There
were plenty of red corpuscles in his blood,
and his heart beat in time with the eternal
laws of right, even though its pulsations
sometimes seemed a little slow and heavy.
It would be well for us if we could get
back into the old way, which proved itself to be the good way, and maintain, as
our fathers did, the sanctity of the family,
the sacredness of the marriage-vow, the
solemnity of the mutual duties binding
parents and children together. From the
households that followed this way have
come men that could rule themselves as
well as their fellows, women that could be

trusted as well as loved. Read the history of such families, and you will understand the truth of the poet's words,—

Self-reverence, self-knowledge, self-control,—
These three alone lead life to sovereign power.

Look around you in the world and see what way it is that has brought your fellow-men to peace and quietness of heart, to security and honour of life. Is it the way of unbridled self-indulgence, of unscrupulous greed, of aimless indolence? or is it the way of self-denial, of cheerful industry, of fair dealing, of faithful service? If true honour lies in the respect and grateful love of one's fellow-men, if true success lies in a contented heart and a peaceful conscience, then the men who have reached the highest goal of life are those who have followed most closely the way to which Jesus Christ points us and in which He goes before us.

III. *Walk therein, and ye shall find rest for your souls.* Right action brings rest.

Rest! Rest! How that word rings like a sweet bell through the turmoil of our age. We are rushing to and fro, destroying rest in our search for it. We drive our automobiles from one place to another, at furious speed, not knowing what we shall do when we get there. We make haste to acquire new possessions, not knowing how we shall use them when they are ours. We are in a fever of new discoveries and theories, not knowing how to apply them when they are made. We feed ourselves upon novel speculations until our heads swim with the vertigo of universal knowledge which changes into the paresis of universal doubt.

But in the hours of silence, the Spirit of Wisdom whispers a secret to our hearts. *Rest depends upon conduct. The result of your life depends upon your choosing the good way, and walking in it.*

And to you I say, my brother-men, choose Christ, for He is the Way. All the strength and sweetness of the best possible human life are embodied in Him. All the truth that is needed to inspire and guide man to noble action and fine character is revealed in Him. He is the one Master al-

together worthy to be served and followed.
Take His yoke upon you and learn of Him,
and ye shall find rest unto your souls.